SILVER·BURDETT

Making Music

Resource Book

Teacher's Edition Part Three
Grade 5

PEARSON

Scott Foresman

Editorial Offices: Glenview, Illinois • Parsippany, New Jersey • New York, New York
Sales Offices: Needham, Massachusetts • Duluth, Georgia • Glenview, Illinois
Coppell, Texas • Sacramento, California • Mesa, Arizona

ISBN: 0-382-36627-1

Copyright © 2005, Pearson Education, Inc.

4 5 6 7 8 9 10 V039 09 08 07 06 05

Program Authors

Jane Beethoven	Marvelene C. Moore
Susan Brumfield	Mary Palmer
Patricia Shehan Campbell	Konnie Saliba
David N. Connors	Will Schmid
Robert A. Duke	Carol Scott-Kassner
Judith A. Jellison	Mary E. Shamrock
Rita Klinger	Sandra L. Stauffer
Rochelle Mann	Judith Thomas
Hunter C. March	Jill Trinka
Nan L. McDonald	

Resource Book Contributing Authors

Jane Beethoven	Activity Masters
Susan Brumfield	Music Reading Worksheets Music Reading Practice
David N. Connors	Orff
Alice-Ann Darrow	Signing
Robert A. Duke	Assessment
Martha F. Hilley	Keyboard
Debbie Burgoon Hines	Pronunciation Practice Guides
Judith A. Jellison	Assessment
Rita Klinger	Music Reading Worksheets Music Reading Practice
Shirley Lacroix	Recorder
Rochelle Mann	Music Reading Worksheets Music Reading Practice
Konnie Saliba	Orff
Julie K. Scott	Orff Recorder
Judith Thomas	Orff
Jill Trinka	Music Reading Worksheets Music Reading Practice
CP Language Institute	Pronunciation Practice Guides

Master Table of Contents

Pronunciation Practice Guides **A-1**

Assessments **B-1**

Graphic Organizers **C-1**

Music Reading Worksheets **D-1**

Music Reading Practice **E-1**

Orff **F-1**

Signing **G-1**

Keyboard **H-1**

Recorder **I-1**

Activity Masters **J-1**

PRONUNCIATION PRACTICE GUIDES

Table of Contents

Laredo A-2

Éliza Kongo A-4

Arirang A-5

Funwa alafia (Welcome, My Friends) . . . A-5

Adelita. A-6

La ciudad de Juaja (The City of Juaja) . . . A-7

A la puerta del cielo (At the Gate of
    Heaven) A-8

Da pacem, Domine (Grant Us Peace) . . . A-9

Ye jaliya da A-9

De colores A-10

Chiapanecas (The Girl from Chiapas) . . A-11

Himmel und Erde (Music Alone
    Shall Live) A-13

Dundai A-14

Jo'ashilá (Walking Together) A-15

La bamba A-16

Las velitas (Candles Burning Bright) . . . A-17

Pollerita A-18

Ego sum pauper (Nothing Do I Own) . . A-19

Las estrellitas del cielo (Stars of the
    Heavens) A-19

Don Alfonso A-20

Meng Jian Nu A-21

Imbabura. A-22

Viva Jujuy. A-23

¡Qué bonita bandera! (What a
    Beautiful Banner!) A-24

Ah ya Zane (Zane from Abedeen) A-26

Tzena, tzena A-27

El carite (The Kingfish) A-30

Se va el caimán (The Alligator) A-31

Bantama kra kro A-34

Yüe liang wan wan (Crescent Moon) . . A-35

Lahk gei mohlee. A-36

Chơi hát bội (The Theater Game) A-37

Ragupati Ragava Raja Ram A-38

La Jesusita A-39

Canción Mixteca (Mixteca Song) A-40

Río, río (River, River) A-42

Zum gali gali A-43

O, Desayo A-44

Uno, dos, y tres (One, Two, and Three) . A-44

Hine mah tov. A-46

Ríu ríu chíu A-46

`Ūlili E A-47

Quâ câù gió bay (The Wind on the
    Bridge) A-49

Oy, Hanuka (O, Chanukah) A-50

Still, Still, Still (Sleep, Dearest Child) . . . A-51

Las Navidades (The Christmas
    Season) A-52

El desembre congelat (Cold
    December) A-53

Hitotsu toya (Temple Bells) A-55

Los reyes de Oriente (The Kings from
    the East) A-56

**Phonetic Pronunciation for
Choral Singing of
Non-English Songs** **A-57**

PRONUNCIATION PRACTICE 1

Laredo

Folk Song from Mexico

Verse 1

Phrase
1. *Ya me voy pa-ra_el La-re-do, mi bien,*
   yah meh voh_ee pah-rah_ehl lah-reh-doh, mee byehn,

2. *Te ven-go_a de-cir a-diós.*
   teh vehn-goh_ah deh-seerr ah-dyohs.

3. *Ya me voy pa-ra_el La-re-do, mi bien,*
   yah meh voh_ee pah-rah_ehl lah-reh-doh, mee byehn,

4. *Te ven-go_a de-cir a-diós.*
   teh vehn-goh_ah deh-seer ah-dyohs.

5. *De a-llá te man-do de-cir, mi bien,*
   deh ah-yah teh mahn-doh deh-seer, mee byehn,

6. *Co-mo se man-cuer-nan dos.*
   koh-moh seh mahn-kwehr-nahn dohs.

7. *De a-llá te man-do de-cir, mi bien,*
   deh ah-yah teh mahn-doh deh-seer, mee byehn,

8. *Co-mo se man-cuer-nan dos.*
   koh-moh seh mahn-kwehr-nahn dohs.

Verse 2

Phrase
1. *To-ma e-sa lla-vi-ta de_o-ro, mi bien,*
   toh-mah eh-sah yah-vee-tah deh_oh-roh, mee byehn,

2. *Abre mi pe-cho y ve-rás:*
   ah_breh mee peh-choh ee veh-rahs:

3. *To-ma e-sa lla-vi-ta de_o-ro, mi bien,*
   toh-mah eh-sah yah-vee-tah deh_oh-roh, mee byehn,

4. *Abre mi pe-cho y ve-rás:*
   ah_breh mee peh-choh ee veh-rahs:

Grade 5, Teacher Edition, page 10

⑤ *Lo mu-cho que yo te quie-ro, mi bien,*
loh moo-choh keh yoh teh kyeh-roh, mee byehn,

⑥ *Y el mal pa-go que me das.*
ee ehl mahl pah-goh keh meh dahs.

⑦ *Lo mu-cho que yo te quie-ro, mi bien,*
loh moo-choh keh yoh teh kyeh-roh, mee byehn,

⑧ *Y el mal pa-go que me das.*
ee ehl mahl pah-goh keh meh dahs.

PRONUNCIATION PRACTICE 2

Éliza Kongo

Traditional Song from Dominica

Phrase

① *Nou ka mou-té*
noo kah moo-tah

② *an-ro-a c'est la-peé*
ahn-roh-ah seh lah-peh

③ *É-li-za Kon-go*
eh-lee-zah kohn-goh

④ *Nou ka mou-té*
noo kah moo-tah

⑤ *an-ro-a c'est la-peé*
ahn-roh-ah seh lah-peh

⑥ *É-li-za Kon-go*
eh-lee-zah kohn-goh

⑦ *Ay jou-joup,*
ah‿ee joo-joop,

⑧ *jou-joup, jou-joup nou ka-man-dé*
joo-joop, joo-joop noo kah-mahn-deh

⑨ *É-li-za Kon-go*
eh-lee-zah kohn-goh

⑩ *Ay pawé-ou,*
ah‿ee pahweh-oo,

⑪ *pawé-ou, pawé-ou mwen ka-vi-ni*
pahweh-oo, pahweh-oo mween kah-vee-nee

⑫ *É-li-za Kon-go.*
eh-lee-zah kohn-goh.

Grade 5, Teacher Edition, page 14

PRONUNCIATION PRACTICE 3

Arirang

Folk Song from Korea

Phrase ① *A-ri-rang, A-ri-rang,*
ah-ree-rahng, ah-ree-rahng,

② *a-ra-ri-yo,*
ahr-rah-ree-yoh,

③ *A-ri-rang ko-ge-ro-nuh-muh-kan-da.*
ah-ree-rahng koh-geh-roo-noh-moh-kahn-dah.

④ *Chung-chun ha-nul-en*
chuhng-chuhn hah-nehl-ehn

⑤ *pyul-do man-ko,*
pyeeah-doh mahn-koh,

⑥ *I-neh ka-sem-en*
ee-neh kah-seeoom-ehn

⑦ *su-sim-do man-ta.*
soo-sheem-doh mahn-tah.

PRONUNCIATION PRACTICE 4

Funwa alafia (Welcome, My Friends)

Folk Song from West Africa

Phrase ① *Fun-wa a-la-fia,*
foon-wah ah-lah-fee_ah,

② *Ah-shay, Ah-shay.*
ah-sheh, ah-sheh.

③ *Fun-wa a-la-fia,*
foon-wah ah-lah-fee_ah,

④ *Ah-shay, Ah-shay.*
ah-sheh, ah-sheh.

PRONUNCIATION PRACTICE 5

Adelita

Folk Song from Mexico

Verse 1 (Unison)

Phrase ① *A-de-li-ta se lla-ma la jo-ven,*
ah-deh-lee-tah seh ya-mah lah hoh-vehn,

② *A quien yo quie-ro_y no pue-do ol-vi-dar.*
ah kyehn yoh kyeh-roh_ee noh pweh-doh ohl-vee-dahr.

③ *Y_en el cam-po yo ten-go_u-na ro-sa,*
ee_yehn ehl kahm-poh yoh tehn-goh_oo-nah roh-sah,

④ *Y con el tiem-po la voy a cor-tar,*
ee kohn ehl tyehm-poh lah voh_ee ah kohr-tahr,

(Harmony)

Phrase ① *Si_A-de-li-ta qui-sie-ra ser mi_es-po-sa*
see_ah-deh-lee-tah kee-syeh-rah sehr mee_ehs-poh-sah

② *Si_A-de-li-ta fue-ra mi mu-jer.*
see_ah-deh-lee-tah fweh-rah mee moo-hehr.

③ *Le com-pra-rí a_un ves-ti-do de se-da,*
leh kohm-prah-ree ah_oon vehs-tee-doh deh seh-dah,

④ *Pa-ra lle-var-la_a bai-lar al cuar-tel.*
pah-rah yeh-vahr-lah bah_ee-lahr ahl kwahr-tehl.

© PEARSON EDUCATION, INC.

Grade 5, Teacher Edition, page 50

PRONUNCIATION PRACTICE 6

La ciudad de Juaja (The City of Juaja)

Folk Song from New Mexico

Verse 1

Phrase

① *Des-de la ciu-dad de Jua-ja,*
dehs-deh lah see‿oo-dahd deh hwah-hah,

② *me man-dan so-li-ci-tar,*
meh mahn-dahn soh-lee-see-tahrr,

③ *que me va-ya que me va-ya,*
keh meh vah-yah keh meh vah-yah,

④ *de‿un te-so-ro a dis-fru-tar.*
deh‿oon teh-soh-roh ah dees-froo-tahr.

Refrain

Phrase

① *¿Qué di-ces, a-mi-go? va-mos*
keh dee-sehs, ah-mee-goh? vah-mohss

② *a ver si di-cen ver-dad,*
ah vehr see dee-sehn vehr-thahth,

③ *Si‿es ver-dad de lo que di-cen*
see‿ehs vehr-thahth deh loh keh dee-sehn

④ *nos que-da-mos por a-llá.*
nohs keh-dah-mohs pohr ah-yah.

Verse 2

Phrase

① *Los ce-rros son de tor-ti-llas,*
lohs seh-rrohs sohn deh tohr-tee-yahs,

② *las que-bra-das de bu-ñue-los,*
lahs keh-brah-dahs deh boo-nweh-lohs,

③ *y las pie-dras, fru-tas cu-bier-tas,*
ee lahs pee‿eh-drahs, froo-tahs koo-byehr-tahs,

④ *pi-nos son los ca-ra-me-los.*
pee-nohs sohn lohs kah-rah-meh-lohs.

PRONUNCIATION PRACTICE 7

A la puerta del cielo
(At the Gate of Heaven)

Folk Song from Spain

Verse 1

Phrase

① *A la puer-ta del cie-lo*
ah lah pwehrr-tah dehl see‿eh-loh

② *ven-den za-pa-tos,*
vehn-dehn sah-pah-tohs,

③ *Pa-ra an-ge-li-tos*
pah-rrah ahn-heh-lee-tohs

④ *que an-dan des-cal-zos,*
keh ahn-dahn dehz-kahl-zohs,

Refrain

Phrase

① *Duér-me-te, ni-ño,*
dwehrr-meh-teh, nee-nyoh,

② *duér-me-te, ni-ño,*
dwehrr-meh-teh, nee-nyoh,

③ *Duér-me-te, ni-ño, a-rrú, a-rrú.*
dwehrr-meh-teh, nee-nyoh,
ah-rroo, ah-rroo.

Verse 2

Phrase

① *A los ni-ños que duer-men*
ah lohs nee-nyohs keh dwehrr-mehn

② *Di‿os los ben-di-ce*
dee‿ohs lohs behn-dee-seh

③ *A las ma-dres que ve-lan*
ah lahs mah-drrehs keh veh-lahn

④ *Di‿os les a-sis-te.*
dee‿ohs lehs ah-sees-teh.

Grade 5, Teacher Edition, page 60

PRONUNCIATION PRACTICE 8

Da pacem, Domine (Grant Us Peace)

Prayer in Latin
Melchior Franck

Phrase ① *Da pa-cem, Do-mi-ne,*
dah pah-chehm, doh-mee-neh,

② *Da pa-cem, Do-mi-ne,*
dah pah-chehm, doh-mee-neh,

③ *in di-e-bus nos-tris.*
een dee-eh-boos nohs-trees.

PRONUNCIATION PRACTICE 9

Ye jaliya da

Folk Song from West Africa

Phrase ① *Ye ja-li-ya da*
yeh djah-lee-yah dah

② *Al-lah le-ga ja-li-ya da.*
ahl-lah leh-kah djah-lee-yah dah.

③ *Ye ja-li-ya da*
yeh djah-lee-yah dah

④ *Al-lah le-ga ja-li-ya da.*
ahl-lah leh-kah djah-lee-yah dah.

PRONUNCIATION PRACTICE 10

De colores

Folk Song from Mexico

Phrase   ①   *De co-lo-res,*
               deh koh-loh-rehs,

       ②   *de co-lo-res se vis-ten los cam-pos*
               deh koh-loh-rehs seh vees-tehn lohs kahm-pohs

       ③   *en la pri-ma-ve-ra,*
               ehn lah pree-mah-veh-rah,

       ④   *De co-lo-res,*
               deh koh-loh-rehs,

       ⑤   *De co-lo-res son los pa-ja-ri-tos*
               deh koh-loh-rehs sohn lohs pah-hah-ree-tohs

       ⑥   *que vie-nen de a-fue-ra,*
               keh vee-eh-nehn deh‿ah-foo‿eh-rah,

       ⑦   *De co-lo-res,*
               deh koh-loh-rehs,

       ⑧   *De co-lo-res es el ar-co i-ris*
               deh koh-loh-rehs ehs ehl ahr-koh ee-rees

       ⑨   *que ve-mos lu-cir,*
               keh veh-mohs loo-seer,

       ⑩   *y por e-so los gran-des*
               ee pohr eh-soh lohs grahn-dehs

       ⑪   *a-mo-res de mu-chos co-lo-res*
               ah-moh-rehs deh moo-chohs koh-loh-rehs

       ⑫   (1st and 2nd endings) *me gus-tan a mí.*
               meh goos-tahn ah mee.

PRONUNCIATION PRACTICE 11

Chiapanecas (The Girl from Chiapas)   *Folk Song from Mexico*

Phrase

① *Un cla-vel co-rté,*
oon clah-vehl kohr-teh,

② *por la sie-rra fui*
pohr lah syeh-rah fwee

③ *ca-mi-ni-to de mi ran-cho.*
kah-mee-nee-toh deh mee rahn-choh.

④ *Co-mo‿el vien-to fue*
koh-moh‿ehl vee‿ehn-toh fweh

⑤ *mi ca-ba-llo fiel*
mee kah-bah-yoh fee-yehl

⑥ *á lle-var-me‿has-ta su la-do,*
ah yeh-vahr-meh‿ah-stah soo lah-doh,

⑦ *Lin-da flor de‿a-bril*
leen-dah flohr deh‿ah-breel

⑧ *to-ma‿es-te cla-vel*
toh-mah‿ehs-teh klah-vehl

⑨ *que te brin-do con pa-sión.*
keh teh breen-doh kohn pah-see‿ohn.

⑩ *No me di-gas no,*
noh meh dee-gahs noh,

⑪ *que‿en tu bo-ca‿es-tá*
keh‿ehn too boh-kah‿eh-stah

⑫ *el se-cre-to de mi‿a-mor.*
ehl seh-kreh-toh deh mee ah-mohr.

⑬ *Cuan-do la no-che lle-gó*
kwahn-doh lah noh-cheh yeh-goh

⑭ *y con su man-to de_a-zul*
ee kohn soo mahn-toh deh_ah-sool

⑮ *el blan-co ran-cho cu-brió*
ehl blahn-koh rahn-choh koo-bree_oh

⑯ *y_a-le-gre_el bai-le_em-pe-zó.*
ee_ah-leh-greh_ehl bah_ee-leh_ehm-peh-soh.

⑰ *Bai-la, mi Chia-pa-ne-ca,*
bah_ee-lah, mee chee_ah-pah-neh-kah,

⑱ *bai-la, bai-la con gar-bo,*
bah_ee-lah, bah_ee-lah kohn gahr-boh,

⑲ *Bai-la sua-ve ra-yo de luz.*
bah_ee-lah swah-veh rah-yoh deh loos.

⑳ *Bai-la, mi Chia-pa-ne-ca,*
bah_ee-lah, mee chee_ah-pah-neh-kah,

㉑ *bai-la, bai-la con gar-bo,*
bah_ee-lah, bah_ee-lah kohn gahr-boh,

㉒ *que_en el bai-le la rei-na_e-res tú,*
kehn ehl bah_ee-leh lah reh-nah_eh-rehs too,

㉓ *Chia-pa-ne-ca gen-til.*
chee_ah-pah-neh-kah gehn-teel.

PRONUNCIATION PRACTICE 12

Himmel und Erde
(Music Alone Shall Live)

Round from Germany

Phrase ① *Him-mel und Er-de*
hihm-mehl oondt eer-duh

② *müss-en ver-gehn;*
moos-ehn fehr-gehn;

③ *a-ber die Mu-si-ca,*
ah-buhr dee moo-see-kah,

④ *a-ber die Mu-si-ca,*
ah-buhr dee moo-see-kah,

⑤ *a-ber die Mu-si-ca*
ah-buhr dee moo-see-kah

⑥ *blei-bet be-stehn.*
bll-beht beh-shtehn.

PRONUNCIATION PRACTICE 13

Dundai

Folk Song from Israel

Verse

Phrase

① *E-rets Yis-ra-el,*
eh-reets ees-rah-ehl,

② *b'-li To-rah.*
beh-lee toh-rah.

③ *Hi k'-guf*
hee kay-goof

④ *b'-li n'sha-ma.*
beh-lee nuhshah-mah.

⑤ *Yal-de Yis-ra-el,*
yahl-deh ees-rah-ehl,

⑥ *lim-du To-rah.*
leem-doo toh-rah.

⑦ *Hiz-ku*
shees-koo

⑧ *im-tsu nish-mat ha-u-ma.*
eems-tsoo nee-shmaht hah-oo-mah.

Refrain

① *Dun-dai, dun-dai,*
doon-dah-ee, doon-dah-ee,

② *dun-dai dai,*
doon-dah-ee dah-ee,

③ *Dun-dai, dun-dai, dun-dai dai.*
doon-dah-ee, doon-dah-ee, doon-dah-ee dah-ee.

Grade 5, Teacher Edition, page 106

PRONUNCIATION PRACTICE 14

Jo'ashilá (Walking Together)

Traditional Song of the Navajo

Phrase

① *Jo-'a-shi-lá,*
joh-ah-shee-lah,

② *Jo-'a-shi-lá,*
joh-ah-shee-lah,

③ *Jo-'a-shi-lá,*
joh-ah-shee-lah,

④ *hei yei' yun ga.*
heh yeh yoon gah.

⑤ *T'oo ga' ni-zhon-ni-go*
toh gah nee-zohn-nee-goh

⑥ *bah ho-zhó lá hei ya' hei',*
bah hoh-tzoh lah heh yah heh,

⑦ *nee ya.*
neh yah.

PRONUNCIATION PRACTICE 15

La bamba

Folk Song from Mexico

Verse 1

Phrase

① *Pa-ra bai-lar la bam-ba.*
pah-rrah bah_ee-lahrr lah bahm-bah.

② *Pa-ra bai-lar la bam-ba-*
pah-rrah bah_ee-lahr lah bahm-bah-

③ *se ne-ce-si-ta un-a po-ca de gra-cia.*
seh neh-seh-see-tah_oon-ah poh-kah deh grrah-see_ah.

④ *Un-a po-ca de gra-cia pa-ra mi pa-ra ti*
oon-ah poh-kah deh grrah-see_ah pah-rrah mee pah-rrah tee

⑤ *y'a a-rri-ba a-rri-ba;*
yah ah-rree-bah ah-rree-bah;

⑥ *y'a-rri-ba y'a-rri-ba por ti se-ré*
yah-rree-bah yah-rree-bah; pohrr tee seh-rreh

⑦ *por ti se-ré por ti se-ré*
pohrr tee seh-rreh pohrr tee seh-rreh

⑧ *yo no soy mar-i-ne-ro.*
yoh noh soh_ee mahrr-ee-neh-rroh.

⑨ *Yo no soy mar-i-ne-ro, soy cap-i-tan;*
yoh noh soh_ee mahrr-ee-neh-rroh, soh_ee kahp-ee-tahn,

⑩ *soy cap-i-tan, soy cap-i-tan.*
soh_ee kahp-ee-tahn, soh_ee kahp-ee-tahn.

Grade 5, Teacher Edition, page 128

PRONUNCIATION PRACTICE 16

Las velitas (Candles Burning Bright)

Folk Song from Mexico

Phrase   ①   *Her-mo-sas ve-li-tas,*
hehr-moh-sahs veh-lee-tahs,

②   *en la_ob-scu-ri-dad.*
ehn lah_ahb-skoo-ree-dahd.

③   *Ha-blan de la_es-tre-lla*
hah-blahn deh lah_ehs-treh-djah

④   *de la Na-vi-dad.*
deh lah nah-vee-dahd.

⑤   *Ved nues-tras ve-li-tas,*
vehd nwehs-trahs veh-lee-tahs,

⑥   *ved que_a-lum-bran bien.*
vehd keh_ah-loom-brahn bee_ehn.

⑦   *Ha-blan de la_es-tre-lla*
hah-blahn deh lah_ehs-treh-djah

⑧   *que bri-lló_en Be-lén.*
keh bree-djoh_ehn beh-lehn.

PRONUNCIATION PRACTICE 17

Pollerita

Folk Song from Bolivia

Phrase ① *Po-lle-ri-ta, po-lle-ri-ta de mi cho-li-ta,*
poh-yeh-ree-tah, poh-yeh-ree-tah deh mee choh-lee-tah,

② *Po-lle-ri-ta, po-lle-ri-ta co-lor ro-si-ta.*
poh-yeh-ree-tah, poh-yeh-ree-tah koh-lohr roh-see-tah.

③ *Que bien se bai-la,*
keh byehn seh bah_ee-lah,

④ *que bien se can-ta,*
keh byehn seh kahn-tah,

⑤ *con mi cha-ran-gui-to.*
kohn mee chah-rahn-ghee-toh.

⑥ *Sa-ra ma-la-gu ta tu*
sah-rah mah-lah-goo tah too

⑦ *ma-na tri-go pe-la-cu*
mah-nah tree-goh peh-lah-koo

⑧ *Ma-na chu-ño pun-ti-co.*
mah-nah choo-noh poon-tee-koh.

⑨ *Que bien se bai-la*
keh byehn seh bah_ee-lah

⑩ *que bien se can-ta*
keh byehn seh kahn-tah

⑪ (1st ending) *con mi cha-ran-qui-to.*
kohn mee chah-rahn-ghee-toh.

⑫ *Que bien se bai-la*
keh byehn seh bah_ee-lah

⑬ *que bien se can-ta*
keh byehn seh kahn-tah

⑭ (2nd ending) *con mi cha-ran-qui-to.*
kohn mee chah-rahn-ghee-toh.

Grade 5, Teacher Edition, page 151

PRONUNCIATION PRACTICE 18

Ego sum pauper (Nothing Do I Own)

Traditional

Phrase ① *E-go sum pau-per,*
eh-goh soom pah-pehrr,

② *Ni-hil ha-be-o*
nee-heel hah-bay-oh

③ *Cor-me-um da-bo.*
kor-meh-oom dah-boh.

PRONUNCIATION PRACTICE 19

Las estrellitas del cielo (Stars of the Heavens)

Folk Song from Spain

Phrase ① *Las es-tre-lli-tas del cie-lo*
lahs ehs-treh-yee-tahs dehl syeh-loh

② *Bri-llan con su luz de pla-ta.*
bree-yahn kohn soo loos deh plah-tah.

③ *San-tia-go las fué sem-bran-do*
sahn-tee-ah-go lahs fweh sehm-brahn-doh

④ *Con sus es-pue-las de pla-ta.*
kohn soos ehs-pweh-lahs deh plah-tah.

PRONUNCIATION PRACTICE 20

Don Alfonso

Folk Song from Spain

Verse 1

Phrase

(1) *De-los ár-bo-les fru-ta-les*
deh-lohs ahr-boh-lehs froo-tah-lehs

(2) *Me gus-ta_el me-lo-co-tón,*
meh goos-tah_ehl meh-loh-koh-tawn,

(3) *Y de los rey-es de Es-pa-ña,*
ee deh lohs reh-yehs deh ehs-pah-nyah,

(4) *Don Al-fon-so de Bor-bón.*
dohn ahl-fahn-soh deh bohr-bawn.

Verse 2

Phrase

(1) *"¿Dón-de vas, Al-fon-so Do-ce?*
dohn-deh vahs, ahl-fahn-soh doh-she?

(2) *¿Dón-de vas, tris-te de ti?"*
dohn-deh vahs, trees-teh deh tee?

(3) *"Voy en bus-ca de Mer-ce-des*
voh_ee ehn boos-kah deh mehr-seh-dehs

(4) *Que_ha-ce tiem-po no la vi."*
keh_ah-seh tyehm-poh noh lah vee.

Verse 3

Phrase

(1) *Ya Mer-ce-des e-stá muer-ta,*
yah mehr-seh-dehs eh-stah mwehr-tah,

(2) *Muer-ta_es-tá que yo la vi,*
mwehr-tah_ehs-tah keh yoh lah vee,

(3) *Cua-tro du-ques la lle-va-ban*
kwah-troh doo-kehs lah yeh-vah-bahn

(4) *Por las ca-lles de Ma-drid.*
pohr lahs kah-yehs deh mah-dreed.

Grade 5, Teacher Edition, page 177

PRONUNCIATION PRACTICE 21

Meng Jian Nu

Folk Song from China

Phrase ① *Zheng yu mei hua,*
djuhng yeh meh_eh hwah,

② *shi xing chung,*
shee seeng chwuhng,

③ *Jia jia hu hu*
jee_ah jee_ah hoo hoo

④ *tian hon deng,*
tee_ehn hohn duhwng,

⑤ *Ran jia zhang fu*
rehn jee-ah djuhng foo

⑥ *tuan yuan ju,*
tuh_ehn yuh_ehn joo,

⑦ *Meng Jian Nu de zhang fu*
mehng zhuhng noo duh djuhng foo

⑧ *zou chan cheng.*
zow chahn chuhwng.

PRONUNCIATION PRACTICE 22

Imbabura

Folk Song from Ecuador

Verse 1, 4

Phrase ① *Im-ba-bu-ra de mi vi-da,*
eem-bah-boo-rah deh mee vee-dah,

② *tú se-rás la pre-fe-ri-da,*
too seh-rahs lah preh-feh-ree-dah,

③ *por-que_a to-das das al-ber-gue*
pohr-keh_ah toh-dahs dahs ahl-behr-geh

④ *co-mo si fue-ran tus hi-jos.*
koh-moh see fweh-rahn toos ee-hohs.

Verse 2

Phrase ① *To-dos los e-cua-to-ria-nos*
toh-dohs lohs eh-kwah-toh-ree_yah-nohs

② *te de-di-ca-mos can-cio-nes,*
teh deh-dee-kah-mohs kahn-see_oh-nehs,

③ *pa-ra tus her-mo-sos la-gos,*
pah-rah toos ehr-moh-sohs lah-gohs,

④ *que nos brin-dan sus ha-la-gos.*
keh nohs breen-dahn soos ah-lah-gohs.

Verse 3

Phrase ① *De mi co-ra-zón la due-ña*
deh mee koh-rah-sohn lah dweh-nyah

② *has de ser, Im-ba-bu-re-ña,*
ahs deh sehr, eem-bah-boo-reh-nyah,

③ *por-que yo_ad-mi-ro tus pren-das,*
pohr-keh djoh_ah-dmee-roh toos prehn-dahs,

④ *tus mu-jé-res y tus flo-res.*
toos moo-heh-rehs ee toos floh-rrehs.

PRONUNCIATION PRACTICE 23

Viva Jujuy

Folk Song from Argentina

Phrase ① *Vi-va Ju-juy, viva la puna,*
vee-vah hoo-hoo-ee, vee-vah lah poo-nah,

② *Viva mi a-ma-da.*
vee-vah mee ah-mah-dah.

③ *Vi-van los ce-rros*
vee-vahn lohs seh-rrohs

④ *pin-ta-rra-jea-dos*
peen-tah-rah-he‿ah-dohs

⑤ *De mi que-bra-da.*
deh mee keh-brah-dah.

⑥ *De mi que-bra-da*
deh mee keh-brah-dah

⑦ *Hu-ma-hua-que-ña.*
hoo-mah-hwah-keh-nyah.

⑧ *No te se-pa-res*
noh teh seh-pah-rehs

⑨ *De mis a-mo-res*
deh mees ah-moh-rehs

⑩ *Tu‿e-res mi due-ña.*
too‿eh-rehs mee dweh-nyah.

PRONUNCIATION PRACTICE 24

¡Qué bonita bandera!
(What a Beautiful Banner!)

Folk Song from Puerto Rico

Verse 1=Unison

Phrase

① *A-zul, blan-ca y co-lo-ra-da,*
ah-sool, blahn-kah ee koh-loh-rah-dah,

② *y en el me-dio tie-ne un es-tre-lla.*
yen ehl meh-dyoh tyeh-neh_oon ehs-treh-jah.

③ *Bo-ni-ta, se-ñor-es,*
boh-nee-tah, seh-nyohr-ehs,

④ *es la ban-de-ra Puer-to-ri-que-ña.*
ehs lah bahn-deh-rah pwehr-toh-ree-keh-nyah.

Refrain=Melody

Phrase

① *¡Qué bo-ni-ta ban-de-ra!*
keh boh-nee-tah bahn-deh-rah!

② *¡Qué bo-ni-ta ban-de-ra!*
keh boh-nee-tah bahn-deh-rah!

③ *¡Qué bo-ni-ta ban-de-ra*
keh boh-nee-tah bahn-deh-rah

④ *es la ban-de-ra Puer-to-ri-que-ña!*
ehs lah bahn-deh-rah
pwehr-toh-ree-keh-nyah!

⑤ *¡Qué bo-ni-ta ban-de-ra!*
keh boh-nee-tah bahn-deh-rah!

⑥ *¡Qué bo-ni-ta ban-de-ra!*
keh boh-nee-tah bahn-deh-rah!

⑦ *¡Qué bo-ni-ta ban-de-ra*
keh boh-nee-tah bahn-deh-rah

⑧ *es la ban-de-ra Puer-to-ri-que-ña!*
ehs lah bahn-deh-rah
pwehr-toh-ree-keh-nyah!

Grade 5, Teacher Edition, page 294

PRONUNCIATION PRACTICE 24 (CONTINUED)

Verse 1=Unison (repeated for Harmony practice)

Phrase

① *A-zul, blan-ca y co-lo-ra-da,*
ah-sool, blahn-kah ee koh-loh-rah-dah,

② *y en el me-dio tie-ne un es-tre-lla.*
yen ehl meh-dyoh tyeh-neh_oon ehs-treh-jah.

③ *Bo-ni-ta, se-ñor-es,*
boh-nee-tah, seh-nyohr-ehs,

④ *es la ban-de-ra Puer-to-ri-que-ña.*
ehs lah bahn-deh-rah pwehr-toh-ree-keh-nyah.

Refrain=Harmony

Phrase

① *¡Qué bo-ni-ta ban-de-ra!*
keh boh-nee-tah bahn-deh-rah!

② *¡Qué bo-ni-ta ban-de-ra!*
keh boh-nee-tah bahn-deh-rah!

③ *¡Qué bo-ni-ta ban-de-ra*
keh boh-nee-tah bahn-deh-rah

④ *es la ban-de-ra Puer-to-ri-que-ña!*
ehs lah bahn-deh-rah pwehr-toh-ree-keh-nyah!

⑤ *¡Qué bo-ni-ta ban-de-ra!*
keh boh-nee-tah bahn-deh-rah!

⑥ *¡Qué bo-ni-ta ban-de-ra!*
keh boh-nee-tah bahn-deh-rah!

⑦ *¡Qué bo-ni-ta ban-de-ra*
keh boh-nee-tah bahn-deh-rah

⑧ *es la ban-de-ra Puer-to-ri-que-ña!*
ehs lah bahn-deh-rah pwehr-toh-ree-keh-nyah!

PRONUNCIATION PRACTICE 25

Ah ya Zane (Zane from Abedeen)

Arabic Folk Song

Phrase

① *Ah ya Zane,*
ah yah zeen,

② *Ah ya Zane,*
ah yah zeen,

③ *Ah ya Zane el A-be-deen*
ah yah zeen ehl ah-bee-deen

④ *Ya ward,*
yah wahrd,

⑤ *Ya ward-im-fet-tah,*
yah wahrd-ihm-feht-tah,

⑥ *bay-nil-ba-sa-teen.*
bee-neel-beh-seh-teen.

Grade 5, Teacher Edition, page 297

© Pearson Education, Inc.

PRONUNCIATION PRACTICE 26

Tzena, tzena

Music by Issachar Miron
Hebrew Words by Yehlel Haggiz;
Arabic Words by Salman Natour

HEBREW

Verse 1

Phrase ① *Tze-na, tze-na, tze-na, tze-na,*
tzehn-nah, tzehn-nah, tzehn-nah, tzehn-nah,

② *ha-ba-not ur-e-na*
hah-bah-naht oor-ee-nah

③ *cha-ve-rim ba-im la-ir.*
hkhah-vah-reem bah-eem lah-eerr.

④ *Al-na, al-na, al-na, al-na,*
ahl-nah, ahl-nah, ahl-nah, ahl-nah,

⑤ *al-na teet-cha-be-na*
ahl-nah teet-hkhah-beh-nah

⑥ *u-miz-mor yach-dav na-shir.*
oo-meez-mohr yahkh-dahv nah-sheerr.

Verse 2

Phrase ① *Tze-na, tze-na, ha-ba-not ur-e-na*
tzehn-nah, tzehn-nah, hah-bah-naht oor-ee-nah

② *cha-ve-rim ba-im la-ir.*
hkhah-vah-reem bah-eem lah-eerr.

③ *Al-na, al-na, al-na, teet-cha-be-na*
ahl-nah, ahl-nah, ahl-nah, teet-hkhah-beh-nah

④ *u-miz-mor yach-dav na-shir.*
oo-meez-mohr yahkh-dahv nah-sheerr.

Verse 3

Phrase ① *Tze-na, tze-na, tze-na, tze-na, tze-na,*
tzehn-nah, tzehn-nah, tzehn-nah, tzehn-nah, tzehn-nah,

② *Tze-na, tze-na, tze-na, tze-na, tze-na,*
tzehn-nah, tzehn-nah, tzehn-nah, tzehn-nah, tzehn-nah,

③ *Tze-na, tze-na, tze-na, tze-na, tze-na,*
tzehn-nah, tzehn-nah, tzehn-nah, tzehn-nah, tzehn-nah,

④ *Tze-na, tze-na, tze-na, tze-na, tze-na,*
tzehn-nah, tzehn-nah, tzehn-nah, tzehn-nah, tzehn-nah,

⑤ *Tze-na!*
tzehn-nah!

ARABIC

Verse 1

Phrase ① *Zei-na, zei-na, zei-na, zei-na,*
zee-nah, zee-nah, zee-nah, zee-nah,

② *Ma-had yuw-kaf bei-ni w'be-na*
mah-hahd yoo-awf beh-nyoo beh-nah

③ *b'lel let t'wa-ad na.*
blee lee twah-ahdt nah.

④ *Yal-la ma'a-na ma'a-na yal-la*
yuh-lah mah-nah mah-nah yuh-lah

⑤ *Nyd-buk deb-ka nur-kus ho-ra*
need-book dahp-kih noor-oos hoh-rrah

⑥ *ma-as ad na.*
mah-uhs ahdt nah.

Verse 2

Phrase ① *Zei-na, zei-na,*
zee-nah, zee-nah,

② *Yal-la ghan-nu ma'a-na*
yuh-lah kuhn-noo mah-nah

③ *ah-lan bi-kom ya-as-ha-ab*
ah-hlahn bih-kohm yuh-ahs-hah-ahb

④ *Zei-na, zei-na,*
zee-nah, zee-nah,

⑤ *Yal-la rud-du ma'a-na*
yuh-lah roodt-doo mah-nah

⑥ *yal-la ya kul lell ah bab*
yuh-lah yuh kool lehl_ah(H) bahb

Verse 3

Phrase ① *Zei-na, zei-na,*
zee-nah, zee-nah,

② *Nur-kus ho-ra*
noorr-oos hoh-rrah

③ *nyd-buk deb-ka yal-la*
need-book dahp-kih yuh-lah

④ *hu-bi ad u'-ma ba-ad-na*
hoo-beh ahd oo-ma bah-hahd-nah

⑤ *Zei-na, zei-na ghan-nu ma'a-na*
zee-nah, zee-nah kahn-noo
mah-nah

⑥ *ghan-nu ma'a-na, ghan-nu*
kahn-noo mah-nah, kahn-noo

⑦ *Zei-na, zei-na, zei-na!*
zee-nah, zee-nah, zee-nah!

El carite (The Kingfish)

Folk Song from Venezuela

Verse

Phrase

① *A-yer sa-lió*
ah-yehrr sah-lee‿oh

② *la lan-cha Nue-va‿Es-par-ta.*
lah lahn-chah noo‿eh-vah‿ehs-pahrr-tah.

③ *Sa-lió con-fia-da*
sah-lee‿oh kohn-fee-ah-dah

④ *a re-co-rrer los ma-res.*
ah rreh-koh-rrehr lohs mah-rrehs.

⑤ *En-con-tró‿un pez*
ehn-kohn-troh‿oon pehz

⑥ *de fuer-zas muy li-je-ro.*
deh foo‿ehr-sahs moo-ee lee-hehr-rroh.

⑦ *Que‿a-ga-rra los an-zue-los*
keh‿ah-gah-rrah lohs ahn-soo‿eh-lohs

⑧ *y re-vien-ta los gua-ra-les.*
ee reh-vee‿ehn-tah lohs gwah-rrah-lehs.

Refrain

① *Co-mo la cos-ta‿es bo-ni-ta,*
koh-moh lah kohs-tah‿ehs boh-nee-tah,

② *Yo me ven-go di-vir-tien-do;*
joh meh vehn-goh dee-veerr-tee‿ehn-doh;

③ *Pe-ro me vie-ne si-guien-do*
peh-rroh meh vee‿eh-neh see-gee-ehn-doh

④ *de fue-ra‿u-na pi-ra-gui-ta.*
deh foo‿eh-rrah‿oo-nah pee-rrah-gwee-tah.

Grade 5, Teacher Edition, page 305

PRONUNCIATION PRACTICE 28

Se va el caimán (The Alligator)

Dance Song from Colombia

Verse 1

Phrase ① *Voy a_em-pe-zar mi re-la-to*
voh_ee ah_ehm-peh-zahr mee reh-lah-toh

② *con a-le-gría_y con a-fán,*
kohn ah-leh-gree_ah_ee kohn ah-fahn,

③ *Voy a_em-pe-zar mi re-la-to*
voh_ee ah_ehm-peh-zahr mee reh-lah-toh

④ *con a-le-gría_y con a-fán,*
kohn ah-leh-gree_ah_ee kohn ah-fahn,

⑤ *Por el rí-o Mag-da-le-na*
pohr ehl ree-oh mahg-dah-leh-nah

⑥ *se_vol-vió_un hom-bre cai-mán,*
seh_vohl-vee_oh_nohm-breh kah_ee-mahn,

⑦ *Por el rí-o Mag-da-le-na*
pohr ehl ree-oh mahg-dah-leh-nah

⑧ *se_vol-vió_un hombre cai-mán.*
seh_vohl-vee_oh_ nohm-breh kah_ee-mahn.

Refrain

Phrase ① *Se va_el cai-mán, Se va_el cai-mán,*
seh vah_ehl kah_ee-mahn, seh vah_ehl kah_ee-mahn,

② *Se va pa-ra Ba-rran-qui-lla,*
seh vah pah-rah bah-rrahn-kee-djah,

③ *Se va_el cai-mán, Se va_el cai-mán,*
seh vah_ehl kah_ee-mahn, seh vah_ehl kah_ee-mahn,

④ *Se va pa-ra Ba-rran-qui-lla.*
seh vah pah-rah bah-rrahn-kee-djah.

© PEARSON EDUCATION, INC.

Grade 5, Teacher Edition, page 306

A-31

⑤ *Se va_el cai-mán, Se va_el cai-mán,*
seh vah_ehl kah_ee-mahn, seh vah_ehl kah_ee-mahn,

⑥ *Se va pa-ra Ba-rran-qui-lla,*
seh vah pah-rah bah-rrahn-kee-djah,

⑦ *Se va_el cai-mán, Se va_el cai-mán,*
seh vah_ehl kah_ee-mahn, seh vah_ehl kah_ee-mahn,

⑧ *Se va pa-ra Ba-rran-qui-lla.*
seh vah pah-rah bah-rrahn-kee-djah.

Verse 2

Phrase ① *Lo que co-me_es-te cai-mán*
loh keh koh-meh_ehs-teh kah_ee-mahn

② *yo le ten-go_ad-mi-ra-ción,*
yoh leh tehn-goh_ahd-mih-rah-see_yohn,

③ *Lo que co-me_es-te cai-mán*
loh keh koh-meh_ehs-teh kah_ee-mahn

④ *yo le ten-go_ad-mi-ra-ción,*
yoh leh tehn-goh_ahd-mih-rah-see_yohn,

⑤ *Co-me que-so_y co-me pan*
koh-meh keh-soh_ee koh-meh pahn

⑥ *con re-fre-scos_de li-món,*
kohn reh-freh-skohs_deh lee-mohn,

⑦ *Co-me que-so_y co-me pan*
koh-meh keh-soh_ee koh-meh pahn

⑧ *con re-fre-scos_de li-món.*
kohn reh-freh-skohs_deh lee-mohn.

PRONUNCIATION PRACTICE 28 (CONTINUED)

Verse 3

Phrase

① *Al o-tro la-do del rí-o*
ahl oh-troh lah-doh dehl ree-oh

② *pes-car-on u-na mo-ja-rra,*
pehs-kah-rohn oo-nah moh-hah-rrah,

③ *Al o-tro la-do del rí-o*
ahl oh-troh lah-doh dehl ree-oh

④ *pes-car-on u-na mo-ja-rra.*
pehs-kah-rohn oo-nah moh-hah-rrah.

⑤ *Y del bu-che le sa-car-on*
ee dehl boo-cheh leh sah-kah-rohn

⑥ *él_que to-ca la gui-ta-rra,*
ehl_keh toh-kah lah gee-tah-rrah,

⑦ *Y del buche le sa-car-on*
ee dehl boo-cheh leh sah-kah-rohn

⑧ *él_que to-ca la gui-ta-rra.*
ehl_keh toh-kah lah gee-tah-rrah.

Bantama kra kro

Song from the Akan People of Ghana

Melody & Harmony

Phrase ① *Ban-ta-ma kra kro,*
bahn-tah-mah krah kraw,

② *meh yeh den na m´an-ya*
meh yeh dehn yah mahn-yah

③ *bi ma-dzi*
bee mehd-zee

④ *Kra kro deh deh iyi*
krah kraw deh deh yih

⑤ *meh yeh den na m´an-ya*
meh yeh dehn yah mahn-yah

⑥ *bi ma-dzi*
bee mehd-zee

⑦ *Kra kro kra kro,*
krah kraw krah kraw,

⑧ *meh yeh den na m´an-ya*
meh yeh dehn yah mahn-yah

⑨ *bi ma-dzi*
bee mehd-zee

⑩ *me nyi si-ka*
meh nyee see-kah

⑪ *meh yeh den na m´an-ya*
meh yeh dehn yah mahn-yah

⑫ *bi ma-dzi.*
bee mehd-zee.

Grade 5, Teacher Edition, page 308

PRONUNCIATION PRACTICE 30

Yüe liang wan wan (Crescent Moon)

Folk Song from China

Phrase   ①   *Pao ma liu liu di shan shang*
pah_oh mah lee-oh dee shahn shahng

②   *Yi duo liu liu di yün yo*
ee dwaw lee-oh lee-oh dee yeen yaw

③   *Duan duan liu liu dee zhao zai*
doh-ahn doh-ahn lee-oh dee dzah-oh dzah_ee

④   *Kang ding liu liu cheng yo*
kahng deeng lee-oh lee-oh dee chung yoh

⑤   *Yüe liang wan wan*
yew-eh lee-ahng wahn wahn

⑥   *kang ding liu liu di cheng yo*
kahng deeng lee-oh lee-oh dee chuhng yoh

PRONUNCIATION PRACTICE 31

Lahk gei mohlee

Folk Song from Taiwan

Phrase

① *Lahk gei moh lee*
lahk geh-ee moh lee

② *jeen jee-ahn shwee,*
jeen jee-ahn shwee,

③ *Long goon sheen jway lee go*
lawng goon sheen jwah-ee lee goh

④ *jeen go jwee.*
jeen goh jwee.

⑤ *Hoh hway lahn dee*
hoh hweh lahn dee

⑥ *sheen shiong dwee,*
sheen shee_ahng dwee,

⑦ *Sheen bean nah moh new-ah lee-goh*
sheen been nah moh noo-ah lee-goh

⑧ *shiong keh kwee.*
shee_ahng keh kwee.

PRONUNCIATION PRACTICE 32

Chơi hát bội (The Theater Game)

Traditional Song from Vietnam

Phrase ① *Rủ nhau ra đám*
roo now rah dahm

② *kìa mú u*
kee-ah moo oo

③ *kìa mú u kìa nọ mú u.*
kee-ah moo oo kee-ah noo moo oo.

④ *Cha kêu mẹ hú*
chah keh‿oo meh ah‿oo

⑤ *mầy còn ngủ tao còn ngủ*
mah‿ee kawn noo tou kawn noo

⑥ *trống lịnh đánh hát bội đó*
trahng lee(n) duh(n) haht boh‿ee duh

⑦ *thức rối còn ngồi đây*
too‿kuh raw‿ee kawn (n)gaw‿ee deh‿ee

⑧ *sao chẳng đi coi họ hát chơi.*
shah-ow chahng dee kaw‿ee haw haht chaw‿ee.

PRONUNCIATION PRACTICE 33

Ragupati Ragava Raja Ram

Traditional Hindu Song

Refrain

Phrase ① *Ra-gu-pa-ti ra-ga-va*
rah-goo-pah-tee rah-gah-vah

② *ra-ja Ram*
rah-jah rahm

③ *Pa-ti-ta pa-va-na*
pah-tee-tah pah-vah-nah

④ *Si-ta Ram.*
see-tah rahm.

Verse 1

Phrase ① *Si-ta Ram jai*
see-tah rahm jah_ee

② *Si-ta Ram,*
see-tah rahm,

③ *Pa-ti-ta pa-va-na*
pah-tee-tah pah-vah-nah

④ *Si-ta Ram.*
see-tah rahm.

Verse 2

Phrase ① *Ish-ware Al-lah*
ee_eesh-wehr ah-lah

② *te-re nam,*
teh-reh nahm,

③ *Sub-ko sun-mut-ti*
sah-buh-koh suhn-muh-tee

④ *de bha-ga-wan.*
deh bah-gah-vahn.

Grade 5, Teacher Edition, page 321

PRONUNCIATION PRACTICE 34

La Jesusita

Folk Song from Mexico

Verse

Phrase ① *Va-mos al bai-le‿y ve-rás que bo-ni-to*
vah-mohs ahl bah‿ee-leh‿ee veh-rahs keh boh-nee-toh

② *Don-de se‿a-lum-bran con vein-te lin-ter-nas,*
dohn-deh seh‿ah-loom-brahn kohn vehn-teh leen-tehr-nahs,

③ *Don-de se bai-lan las dan-zas mo-der-nas,*
dohn-deh seh bah‿ee-lahn lahs dahn-sahs moh-dehr-nahs,

④ *Don-de se bai-la de mu-cho va-ci-lón.*
dohn-deh seh bah‿ee-lah deh moo-choh vah-see-lohn.

Refrain

Phrase ① *Y quié-re-me, Je-su-si-ta,*
ee kyeh-reh-meh, heh-soo-see-tah,

② *Y quié-re-me, por fa-vor;*
ee kyeh-reh-meh, pohr fah-vohr;

③ *Y mi-ra que soy tu‿a-man-te*
ee mee-rah keh soh‿ee too-ah-mahn-teh

④ *Y se-gu-ro ser-vi-dor.*
ee seh-goo-roh sehr-vee-dohr.

PRONUNCIATION PRACTICE 35

Canción Mixteca (Mixteca Song)

Words and Music by José López Alavés

Melody & Harmony

Phrase ① *!Que le-jos es-toy*
keh leh-hos ehs-toh‿ee

② *del sue-lo don-de‿he na-ci-do!*
dehl sweh-loh dohn-deh nah-see-thoh!

③ *In-men-sa nos-tal-gia‿in-va-de*
een-mehn-sah noh-stahl-hyeh‿een-vah-theh

④ *mi pen-sa-mien-to!*
mee pehn-sah-myehn-toh!

⑤ *Y‿al ver-me tan so-lo‿y tris-te*
yahl vehr-meh tahn soh-loh‿ee tree-steh

⑥ *cual ho-ja‿al vien-to,*
kwahl oh-hahl vyehn-toh,

⑦ *qui-sie-ra llo-rar,*
kee-syeh-rah djoh-rahr,

⑧ *qui-sie-ra mo-rir de sen-ti-mien-to.*
kee-syeh-rah moh-reer deh sehn-tee-myehn-toh.

⑨ *!Oh tie-rra del sol!*
oh tyeh-rrah dehl sohl!

⑩ *Sus-pi-ro por ver-te*
Soo-spee-roh pohrr vehr-teh

⑪ *a-ho-ra que le-jos*
ah-oh-rah keh leh-hohs

⑫ *yo vi-vo sin luz sin a-mor.*
yoh vee-voh seen loos seen ah-mohr.

⑬ *Y_al ver-me tan so-lo_y tris-te*
yahl vehr-meh tahn soh-loh_ee tree-steh

⑭ *cual ho-ja_al vien-to,*
kwahl oh-hahl vyehn-toh,

⑮ *qui-sie-ra llo-rar,*
kee-syeh-rah djoh-rahr,

⑯ *qui-sie-ra mo-rir de sen-ti-mien-to.*
kee-syeh-rah moh-reer deh sehn-tee-myehn-toh.

PRONUNCIATION

Zum gali ga

Refrain
Phrase ① *Zum ga-li*
zoom gal

② *zum ga-li*
zoom ga

③ *Zum ga-l*
zoom ga

Verse 1
Phrase ① *He-cha-l*
heh-khal

② *A-vo-dah*
ah-voh-

③ *A-vo-dah*
ah-voh-

④ *He-cha-l*
heh-kha

Verse 2
Phrase ① *He-cha-l*
heh-kha

② *Ha-b'tu-*
hahb-to

③ *Ha-sha-*
hah-sha

④ *Ha'-a-m*
hah-ah-

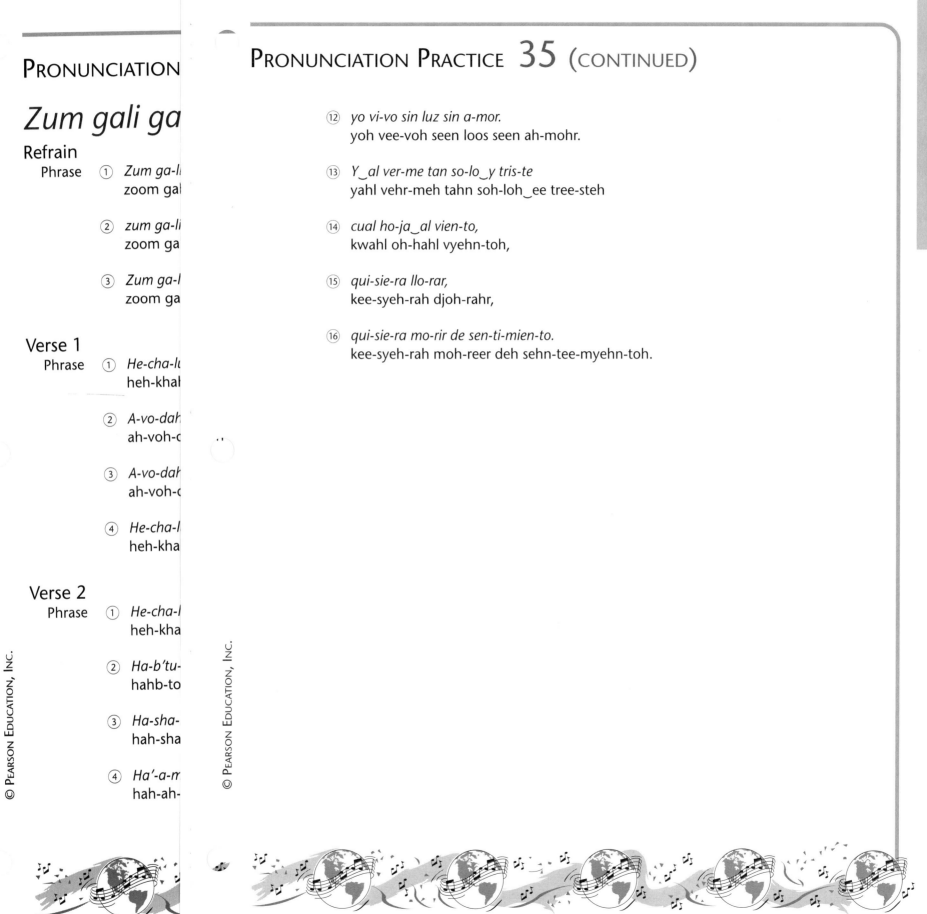

O, Desayo

Folk Song from Angola

Phrase
1. *O, Des-ay-o!*
   oh, deh-sI-yoh!

2. *O, Des-ay-o!*
   oh, deh-sI-yoh!

3. *O, Des-ay-o! Me-ni-na,*
   oh, deh-sI-yoh! meh-nee-nah,

4. *O, Des-ay-o!*
   oh, deh-sI-yoh!

Uno, dos, y tres
(One, Two, and Three)

Words and Music by Rafael Ortiz

Phrase
1. *Al tam-bor ma-yor de‿a-lan-te*
   ahl tahm-bohr mah‿yohr deh‿ah-lahn-teh

2. *no‿hay qui-en lo pue-da‿i-gua-lar*
   noh‿ah‿ee kee-ehn loh pweh-dah‿ee-gwah-lahr

3. *con su rit-mo fas-ci-nán-te*
   kohn soo reet-moh fah-see-nahn-teh

4. *de mi Cu-ba tro-pi-cal.*
   deh mee koo-bah troh-pee-kahl.

5. *Cuen-ten los pa-sos*
   kwehn-tehn lohs pah-sohs

Left column (partially obscured)

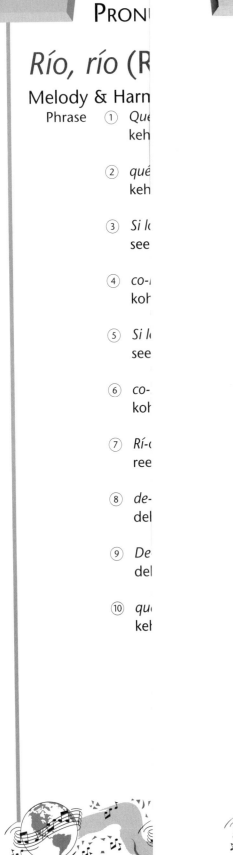

PRON

Río, río (R

Melody & Harn

Phrase
1. *Qué*
   keh

2. *qué*
   keh

3. *Si l*
   see

4. *co-*
   koh

5. *Si l*
   see

6. *co-*
   koh

7. *Rí-*
   ree

8. *de-*
   del

9. *De*
   del

10. *qu*
    keh

⑥ *que_a-quí lle-ga-mos.*
keh_ah-kee djeh-gah-mohs.

⑦ *U-no, dos, y tres*
oo-noh, dohs, ee trehs

⑧ *que pa-so más ché-ve-re,*
keh pah-soh mahs cheh-veh-reh,

⑨ *qué pa-so más ché-ve-re,*
keh pah-soh mahs cheh-veh-reh,

⑩ *el de mi con-ga es,*
ehl deh mee kohn-gah ehs,

⑪ *el de mi con-ga es, el de mi con-ga es.*
ehl deh mee kohn-gah ehs, ehl deh mee kohn-gah ehs.

PRONUNCIATION PRACTICE 40

Hine mah tov

Hebrew Folk Song

Phrase ① *Hi-ne mah tov*
hee-neh mah tohv

② *u-mah na-'im*
oo-mah nah-eem

③ *she-vet a-chim*
sheh-veht ah-hkheem

④ *gam ya-chad!*
gahm yah-hkhahd!

⑤ *Hi-ne mah tov u-mah na-'im*
hee-neh mah tohv ooh-mah nah-eem

⑥ *she-vet a-chim gam ya-chad!*
sheh-veht ah-hkheem gahm yah-hkhahd!

PRONUNCIATION PRACTICE 41

Ríu ríu chíu

Sixteenth Century Carol from Spain

Refrain
Phrase ① *Rí-u rí-u chí-u*
rree-oo rree-oo chee-oo

② *la guar-da ri-be-ra,*
lah gwahr-dah ree-beh-rrah,

③ *Dios guar-do el lo-bo*
dee‿ohs gwahr-doh ehl loh-boh

④ *de nues-tra cor-de ra.*
deh noo‿ehs-trrah kor-deh rrah.

© PEARSON EDUCATION, INC.

     Grade 5, Teacher Edition, pages 430 and 434

ʻŪlili E

Traditional Song from Hawaii

Verse 1

Phrase

① *Ho-ne a-na ko le-o*
hoh-neh ah-nah koh leh-oh

② *e ʻu-li-li e*
eh oo-lee-lee eh

③ *E-ka-hi ma-nu*
eh-kah-hee mah-noo

④ *no-ho a-ʻe kai*
noh-hoh ah-eh kah‿ee

⑤ *Ki-ā-ʻi ma ka lae*
kee-ah-ee mah kah lah-eh

⑥ *o Ke-ka-ha*
oh keh-kah-hah

⑦ *ʻO-i-a kai u-a*
oh-ee-ah kah‿ee oo-ah

⑧ *la-na ma-li-e.*
lah-nah mah-lee-eh.

⑨ *ʻŪ-li-li e,*
oo-lee-lee eh,

Vocal Part 2 and Melody
(Vocal Part 2)

Phrase

① *ʻA-ha-ha-na ʻu-li-li ʻe-he-he-ne*
ah-hah-hah-nah ee-lee-lee
eh-heh-heh-neh

② *ʻū-li-li ʻa-ha-ha-na*
oo-lee-lee ah-hah-hah-nah

(Melody)

③ *ʻŪ-li-li ho-ʻi*
oo-lee-lee hoh-ee

④ *ʻE-he-he-ne ʻū-li-li ʻa-ha-ha-na*
eh-heh-heh-neh oo-lee-lee
ah-hah-hah-nah

⑤ *ʻū-li-li ʻe-he-he-ne*
oo-lee-lee eh-heh-heh-neh

⑥ *ʻŪ-li-li ʻŪ-li-li*
oo-lee-lee oo-lee-lee

⑦ *ho-lo ho-lo ka-ha-kai e,*
hoh-loh hoh-loh
kah-hah-kah‿ee eh,

⑧ *ʻO-i-a kai u-a*
oh-ee-ah kah‿ee oo-ah

⑨ *la-na mā-li-e*
lah-nah mah-lee-eh

⑩ *ʻŪ-li-li e,*
oo-lee-lee eh,

Vocal Part 3 and Melody

(Vocal Part 3)

Phrase ① 'A-ha-ha-na 'ū-li-li 'e-he-he-ne
ah-hah-hah-nah ee-lee-lee
eh-heh-heh-neh

② 'ū-li-li 'a-ha-ha-na
oo-lee-lee ah-hah-hah-nah

(Melody)

③ 'Ū-li-li ho-'i
oo-lee-lee hoh-ee

(Vocal Part 3)

④ 'E-he-he-ne 'ū-li-li 'a-ha-ha-na
eh-heh-heh-neh oo-lee-lee
ah-hah-hah-nah

⑤ 'ū-li-li 'e-he-he-ne
oo-lee-lee eh-heh-heh-neh

⑥ 'Ū-li-li 'Ū-li-li
oo-lee-lee oo-lee-lee

⑦ ho-lo ho-lo ka-ha-kai e,
hoh-loh hoh-loh
kah-hah-kah‿ee eh,

⑧ 'O-i-a kai u-a
oh-ee-ah kah‿ee oo-ah

⑨ la-na mā-li-e
lah-nah mah-lee-eh

⑩ 'ū-li-li e,
oo-lee-lee eh,

Verse 2

Phrase ① Ho-ne a-na ko le-o
hoh-neh ah-nah koh leh-oh

② e kō-le-a e
eh koh-leh-ah eh

③ Pe-he-a 'o Ka-hi-ki?
peh-heh-ah oh kah-hee-kee?

④ Mai-ka 'i no.
mah‿ee-kah ee noh.

⑤ 'O-i-a 'āi-na
oh-ee-ah ah‿yee-nah

⑥ u-lu-we-hi-we-hi
oo-loo-veh-hee-veh-hee

⑦ I hu-i pū 'i-a
ee hoo-ee poh ee-ah

⑧ me ke o nao-na.
meh keh oh nah‿oo-nah.

PRONUNCIATION PRACTICE 43

Quâ cấu gió bay
(The Wind on the Bridge)

Folk Song from Vietnam

Verse 1

Phrase ① *Yêu nhau cờ-i áo ý_a cho nhau.*
ee_ew nyah_oo koh-ee ow ee_ah tchoh nyah_oo.

② *Về nhà dối rằng cha dối mẹ a ý_a.*
veh nyah zoh_ee zuhng tchah zoh_ee meh_eh ah ee_ah.

③ *Rằng a ý_a qua cấu. Rằng a ý_a qua cầu.*
zuhng ah ee_ah kwah kuh_oh. zuhng ah ee_ah kwah kuh_oh.

Refrain

Phrase ① *Tình tình tình gió bay,*
teen teen teen soh_hoh beh_ee,

② *Tình tình tình gió bay.*
teen teen teen soh_hoh beh_ee.

Verse 2

Phrase ① *Yêu nhau cờ-i nón y_a cho nhau.*
ee_ew nyah_oo koh-ee naw(tn)
ee_ah tchoh nyah_oo.

② *Về nhà dối rằng cha dối mẹ a ý_a.*
veh nyah zoh_ee zuhng tchah
zoh_ee meh_eh ah ee_ah.

③ *Rằng a ý_a qua cấu. Rằng a ý_a qua cầu.*
zuhng ah ee_ah kwah kuh_oh.
zuhng ah ee_ah kwah kuh_oh.

Verse 3

Phrase ① *Yêu nhau cờ-i nhan y_a cho nhau.*
ee-ew nyah_oo kuhr-ee nyuhr(n)
ee_ah tchoh nyah_oo.

② *Vế nhà dối rằng cha dối mẹ a ý_a.*
veh nyah zoh-ee zuhng tchah zoh
_ee meh_eh ah ee_ah.

③ *Rằng a ý_a qua cầu. Rằng a ý_a qua cầu.*
zuhng ah ee_ah kwah kuh_oh.
zuhng ah ee_ah kwah kuh_oh.

Refrain

Phrase ① *Tình tình tình gió bay,*
teen teen teen soh_hoh beh_ee,

② *Tình tình tình gió bay.*
teen teen teen soh_hoh beh_ee.

Final Refrain

Phrase ① *Tình tình tình dánh ro-i,*
teen teen teen dah-(n) zuh-ee,

② *Tình tình tình dánh ro-i.*
teen teen teen dah-(n) zuh-ee.

Oy, Hanuka (O, Chanukah)

Yiddish Folk Song

Verse 1

Phrase

① *Oy Ha-nu-ka, Oy Ha-nu-ka, a yom-tov a shey-ner,*
oh_ee khah-nih-keh, oh_ee khah-nih-keh, ah yuhn-tehv ah sheh_ee-nehrr,

② *A lu-sti-ker, a frey-le-kher, ni-to nokh a-zoi-ner.*
ah loo-stih-kehr, ah free-leh-kher, nih-toh nohkh ah-zoh_ee-nehrr.

③ *Al-le nakht in drey-dl shpi-ln mir,*
ah-leh nahkt ihn dreh_ee-duhl shpih-(ln) meerr,

④ *Zu-dik hey-se lat-kes, est on a shir.*
zoo-dihk heh_ee-seh laht-kehs, ehst ohn ah sheerr.

⑤ *Gesh-vin-der, tsindt kin-der,*
gehsh-vihn-dehr, tsihndt kihn-dehrr,

⑥ *Dee di-nin-ke likh-te-lekh ohn.*
dee dee-nihn-keh lihkh-teh-lekh ohn.

⑦ *Zingt "Al Ha-ni-sim," loibt Gott far di ni-sim,*
zih(ng)t ahl hah-nih-suhm, loh_eebt guht fahr dee nih-suhm,

⑧ *Un kumt gi-kher tan-tsn in kohn.*
uhn-kuhmt gih-khehr tahn-tsn ihn kohn.

Second Ending

① *Un kumt gi-kher tan-tsn in kohn.*
uhn-kuhmt gih-khehr tahn-tsn ihn kohn.

PRONUNCIATION PRACTICE 45

Still, Still, Still (Sleep, Dearest Child)

Traditional Carol from Austria

Verse 1

Phrase

① *Still, still, still,*
shteel, shteel, shteel,

② *weils Kind-lein schlaf-en will.*
vI_ehls keend-lah_een shlahf-ehn veel.

③ *Ma-ri-a tut es*
mah-ree-ah toot ehs

④ *nie-der-sing-en,*
nee-dehr-tzeeng-ehn,

⑤ *sei-ne gro-sse*
tzI_ee-neh kgroh-seh

⑥ *Lieb dar-bring-en.*
leepb dahr-breeng-ehn.

⑦ *Still, still, still,*
shteel, shteel, shteel,

⑧ *weils Kind-lein schla-fen will.*
vI_ehls keend-lah_een shlahf-ehn veel.

Verse 2

Phrase

① *Schlaf, schlaf, schlaf,*
shlahf, shlahf, shlahf,

② *mein lie-bes Kind-lein schlaf.*
mI_een lee-behs keend-lah_een shlahf.

③ *Die Eng-el tun schön*
dee ehng-ehl toon shuh(r)n

④ *mu-si-zie-ren*
moo-zee-tzee-rehn

⑤ *bei dem Kind-lein*
bI_ee dehm keend-lI_een

⑥ *ju-bi-lie-ren.*
yoo-bee-lee-rehn.

⑦ *Schlaf, schlaf, schlaf,*
shlahf, shlahf, shlahf,

⑧ *mein lie-bes Kind-lein schlaf.*
mI_een lee-behs keend-lah_een
shlahf.

PRONUNCIATION PRACTICE 46

Las Navidades
(The Christmas Season)

Traditional from Puerto Rico

Verse 1

Phrase

1. *Por fin lle-ga-ron*
   pohr feen djeh-gah-rrohn

2. *las Na-vi-da-des*
   lahs nah-vee-thah-thehs

3. *las fies-tas rea-les*
   lahs fee_eh-stahs rreh_ah-lehs

4. *de nues-tro lar.*
   theh noo_eh-stroh lahrr.

5. *Fies-ta de to-dos*
   fee_eh-stah theh toh-thohs

6. *Nues-tros an-he-los,*
   noo_eh-strohs ahn-eh-lohs,

7. *nues-tros des ve-los, y
   nues-tro_a fán.*
   noo_eh-strohs thehs veh-lohs,
   ee noo_eh-stroh_ah-fahn.

Verse 2

Phrase

1. *Con tam-bo-ri-les,*
   kohn tahm-bohr-ee-lehs,

2. *güi-ro_y ma-ra-cas,*
   gwee-rroh_ee mah-rah-kahs,

3. *mi se-re-na-ta*
   mee seh-reh-nah-tah

4. *a-le-gre va.*
   ah-leh-greh bah.

5. *De-se-o_a to-dos*
   theh-seh_oh ah toh-thohs

6. *por des-pe-di-da*
   pohrr theh-speh-thee-thah

7. *a-ños de vi-da_y fe-li-ci-dad.*
   ah-nyohs theh vee-thah_ee feh-
   lee-see-thahth.

Grade 5, Teacher Edition, page 472

PRONUNCIATION PRACTICE 47

El desembre congelat (Cold December)

Fifteenth-century Melody from Catalonia

Verse 1

Phrase

① *El de-sem-bre con-ge-lat,*
ahl deh-zehm-breh kohn-djeh-laht,

② *Con-fós es re-ti-ra.*
kohm-fooz ehs reh-dee-rah.

③ *A-bril de flors co-ro-nat,*
ah-breel deh flohs koh-roo-naht,

④ *Tot el món ad-mi-ra.*
toht ehl mohn aht-mee-rah.

⑤ *Quan en un jar-dí d'a-mor*
kwahn ehn oon djahr-dee dah-mohr

⑥ *Neix u-na di-vi-na flor.*
nehsh oo-nuh dee-vee-nah floh.

⑦ *D'u-na ro ro ro, d'u-na sa sa sa,*
doo-nah rroh rroh rroh, doo-nah sah sah sah,

⑧ *d'u-na ro, d'u-na sa, d'u-na ro-sa bel-la,*
doo-nah rroh, doo-nah sah, doo-nah rroh-zah beh-yah,

⑨ *Fe-cun-da_i pon-cel-la.*
fah-koon-deh_ee poon-seh-yah.

PRONUNCIATION PRACTICE 47 (CONTINUED)

Verse 2

Phrase

① *El pri-mer pa-re caus-à,*
ahl pree-meh pah-reh kow-zah,

② *La nit te-ne-bro-sa.*
lah neet teh-neh-broh-zah.

③ *Que_a tot el món o-fus-cà*
kuh toht ehl mohn oh-foos-kah

④ *La vis-ta pen-o-sa.*
lah vees-tah peh-noh-zah.

⑤ *Mes en u-na mit-ja-nit,*
mehz ehn oo-nah meed-jah-neet,

⑥ *bri-lla_el sol que n'és eix-it.*
bree-yuhl sohl kuh nehz uh-sheet.

⑦ *D'u-na bel bel bel, d'u-na la la la,*
doo-nah behl behl behl, doo-nah yah yah yah,

⑧ *d'u-na bel, d'u-na la, d'u-na bel-la_au-ro-ra*
doo-nah behl, doo-nah yah, doo-nah behl -yah_ow-roh-rah

⑨ *que_el cel en-a-mo-ra.*
kuhl sehl eh-nuh-moh-rah.

PRONUNCIATION PRACTICE 48

Hitotsu toya (Temple Bells)

Folk Song from Japan

Verse 1

Phrase

① *Hi-to-tsu to-ya,*
hee-toh-tsoo toh-yah,

② *Hi-to-yo a-ku-re-ba*
hee-toh-yah uh-koo-ruh-bah

③ *Ni-gi-ya-ka de,*
nee-geh-yah-kah deh,

④ *Ni-gi-ya-ka de,*
nee-geh-yah-kah deh,

⑤ *O-ka-za-ri ta-te ta-ru*
oh-kah-zah-ree tah-tuh tah-roo

⑥ *Ma-tsu-ka-za-ri,*
mah-tsoo-kah-zah-ree,

⑦ *Ma-tsu-ka-za-ri.*
mah-tsoo-kah-zah-ree.

Verse 2

Phrase

① *Fu-ta-tsu to-ya,*
foo-tah-tsoo toh-yah,

② *Fu-ta-ba no ma-tsu wa*
foo-tah-bah noh mah-tsoo wah

③ *I-ro yo te,*
ee-roh yoh-oo teh,

④ *I-ro yo te.*
ee-roh yoh-oo teh.

⑤ *Sa-n-ga-i ma-tsu wa*
sah-(n)-gah-ee mah-tsoo wah

⑥ *Ka-su-ga ya-ma,*
kah-soo-gah yah-mah,

⑦ *Ka-su-ga ya-ma.*
kah-soo-gah yah-mah.

Verse 3

Phrase

① *Mit-tsu to-ya,*
meet-tsoo toh-yah,

② *Mi-na-san ko-na hi wa*
mee-nah-sah-(n) koh-nah hee wah

③ *Ra-ku-a-so-bi,*
rah-koo-ah-soh-bee,

④ *Ra-ku-a-so-bi,*
rah-koo-ah-soh-bee,

⑤ *Fu-ru-sa-ki ko-ma-do de*
foo-roo-sah-kee koh-mah-doh deh

⑥ *Ha-ne o tsu-ku,*
hah-neh oh tsoo-koo,

⑦ *Ha-ne o tsu-ku.*
hah-neh oh tsoo-koo.

PRONUNCIATION PRACTICE 49

Los reyes de Oriente
(The Kings from the East)

Aguinaldo from Puerto Rico

Phrase   ①   *De tie-rra le-ja-na*
deh tyeh-rrah leh-hah-nah

②   *ve-ni-mos a ver-te,*
veh-nee-mohs ah vehrr-teh,

③   *Nos sir-ve de guí-a*
nohs seer-veh deh ghee-ah

④   *la‿es-tre-lla de‿O-rien-te.*
lah‿ehs-treh-jah deh‿oh-ryehn-teh.

⑤   *¡Oh, bri-llan-te‿es-tre-lla*
oh, bree-jan-teh‿ehs-treh-jah

⑥   *que‿a-nun-cias la‿au-ro-ra,*
keh‿ah-noon-syahs lou-roh-rah,

⑦   *No me fal-te nun-ca*
noh meh fahl-teh noon-kah

⑧   *tu luz bien-he-cho-ra!*
too loos byehn-eh-choh-rah!

PRONUNCIATION PRACTICE 50

Phonetic Pronunciation for Choral Singing of Non-English Songs

ah	as in f<u>a</u>ther
ah_ee	as in l<u>igh</u>t (diphthong; a long *ah* sound with a hint of *ee* at close)
aw	as in <u>awe</u>
eh_ee	as in d<u>ay</u> (diphthong; a long *eh* sound with a hint of *ee* at close)
b	as in <u>b</u>utton
ch	as in <u>ch</u>urch
d	as in <u>d</u>ad
dj	as in ju<u>dg</u>e
ee	as in s<u>ee</u>d
eh	as in l<u>e</u>t
ew	used for French u (pronounce a bright *ee* and round the lips as if to whistle)
f	as in <u>f</u>ace
g	as in <u>g</u>oat
h	as in <u>h</u>at
hkh	guttural, aspirant <u>h</u> of German, Hebrew <u>ch</u>, and Spanish <u>j</u>
ih	as in f<u>i</u>t
I	as in l<u>i</u>ght (a harsh *i* sound, where possible an *ah_ee* has been suggested for singing the I sound)
k	as in <u>k</u>ite
l	as in <u>l</u>et
ll	prolonged <u>l</u> sound
m	as in <u>m</u>an
(m)	French nasal <u>m</u>, not articulated

	as a distinct letter but as an open nasal sound
n	as in <u>n</u>ote
(n)	French nasal <u>n</u>, not articulated as a distinct letter, but as an open nasal sound
(ng)	as in sa<u>ng</u> (sometimes sounded as a prolonged nasal tone)
oh	as in t<u>o</u>ne
oo	as in sp<u>oo</u>n
ow	as in p<u>ow</u>der
p	as in <u>p</u>at
r	as in <u>r</u>an
(r)	as in tu<u>r</u>n (combined with another vowel sound in German)
rr	rolled <u>r</u>
rrrr	extended trilled <u>r</u>
s	as in <u>s</u>ong
t	as in <u>t</u>ell
th	as in <u>th</u>at
thh	as in fea<u>th</u>er
uh	as in <u>u</u>p
v	as in <u>v</u>an
w	as in <u>w</u>ay
wh	as in <u>wh</u>at
y	as in <u>y</u>es (not a vowel sound)
z	as in <u>z</u>one
zh	as in a<u>z</u>ure

Teacher Notes

ASSESSMENT
Table of Contents

UNIT 1

Show What You Know! B-2

Review, Assess, Perform, Create B-3

    What Do You Know? B-3

    What Do You Hear? 1A. B-3

    What Do You Hear? 1B. B-4

    What You Can Do. B-4

UNIT 2

Show What You Know! B-5

Review, Assess, Perform, Create B-6

    What Do You Know? B-6

    What Do You Hear? 2. . . . . B-7

    What You Can Do. B-7

UNIT 3

Show What You Know! B-8

Review, Assess, Perform, Create B-9

    What Do You Know? B-9

    What Do You Hear? 3. . . . . B-10

    What You Can Do. B-10

UNIT 4

Show What You Know! B-11

Review, Assess, Perform, Create B-12

    What Do You Know? B-12

    What Do You Hear? 4. . . . . B-13

    What You Can Do. B-14

UNIT 5

Show What You Know! B-15

Review, Assess, Perform, Create B-16

    What Do You Know? B-16

    What Do You Hear? 5A. B-16

    What Do You Hear? 5B. B-16

    What You Can Do. B-17

UNIT 6

Show What You Know! B-18

Review, Assess, Perform, Create B-19

    What Do You Know? B-19

    What Do You Hear? 6A. B-19

    What Do You Hear? 6B. B-19

    What You Can Do. B-20

RUBRICS AND CHECKLIST

Introduction for the Music Teacher . . . B-22

Singing B-23

Playing Instruments B-24

Reading B-25

Moving and Improvising B-26

Composing/Arranging/Notating B-27

Listening B-28

Assessment Answer Key ***B-29***

ASSESSMENT 1: UNIT 1

Using a rhythm instrument of your choice, **play** the following patterns.

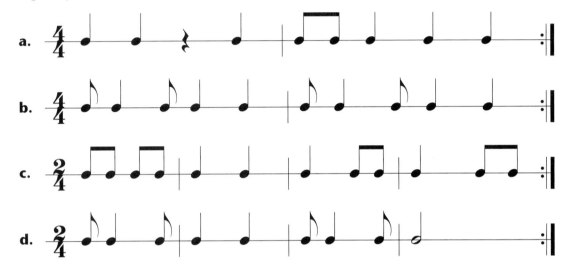

Which pattern or patterns use syncopation? _____

Create and **perform** new response melodies for "Bound for South Australia." Choose your notes from the C-pentatonic scale (C-D-E-G-A).

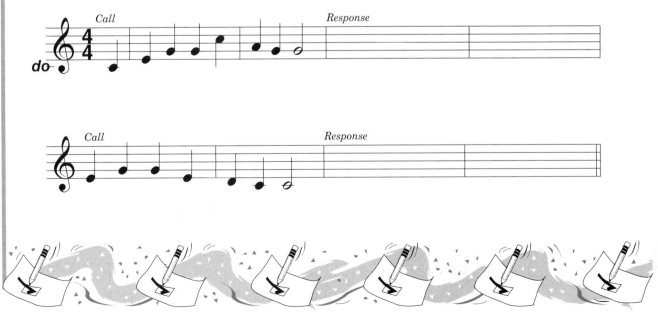

Grade 5, Teacher Edition, pages 17 and 27

ASSESSMENT 1: UNIT 1 (CONTINUED)

Review, Assess, Perform, Create

What Do You Know?

1. Match each dynamic symbol with the correct name and definition. Place the letters of your answers in the spaces provided.

a. *p* ____ *forte* (loud)

b. *mf* ____ *piano* (soft)

c. *ff* ____ *pianissimo* (very soft)

d. *mp* ____ *fortissimo* (very loud)

e. *pp* ____ *mezzo forte* (medium loud)

f. *f* ____ *mezzo piano* (medium soft)

2. Look at the melody for "This Train," on page 27. Where is *do*? Notate *do* on the staff. Identify and count the following pitch syllables.

a. Count all the notes that are called *so*. ____

b. Count all the notes that are called *re*. ____

c. Count all the notes that are called *la*. ____

d. Count all the notes that are called *do*. ____

What Do You Hear? 1A Vocal Timbre

Listen to the following vocal timbres. Identify the voice(s) you hear in each listening selection. Circle your answers.

1. male solo   female solo

2. children's chorus   mixed adult chorus

3. solo and chorus   chorus   solo

ASSESSMENT 6: UNIT 6 (CONTINUED)

What You Can Do

Create a 12-bar Blues Song

- Compose your own 12-bar blues song (see the form of "Good Mornin', Blues," page 224, for an example).

- Notate your melody in the key of C.

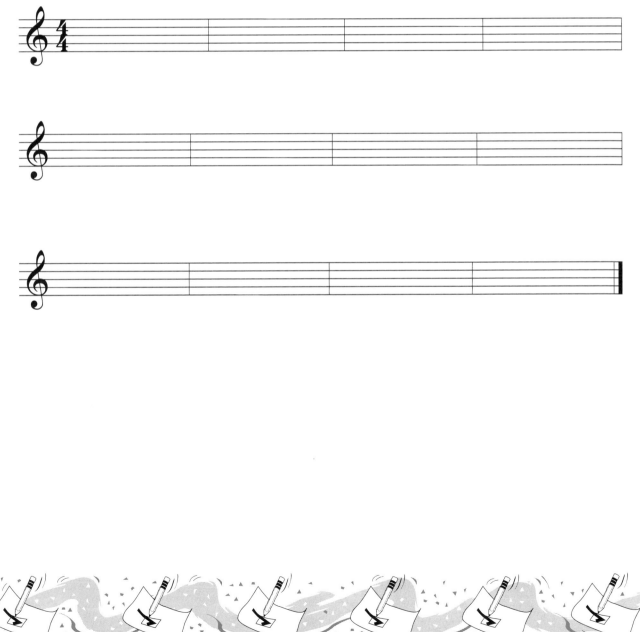

ASSESSMENT 1: UNIT 1 (CONTINUED)

Review, Assess, Perform, Create

What Do You Know?

1. Match each dynamic symbol with the correct name and definition. Place the letters of your answers in the spaces provided.

a. *p*   _____ *forte* (loud)

b. *mf*   _____ *piano* (soft)

c. *ff*   _____ *pianissimo* (very soft)

d. *mp*   _____ *fortissimo* (very loud)

e. *pp*   _____ *mezzo forte* (medium loud)

f. *f*   _____ *mezzo piano* (medium soft)

2. Look at the melody for "This Train," on page 27. Where is *do*? Notate *do* on the staff. Identify and count the following pitch syllables.

a. Count all the notes that are called *so*. _____

b. Count all the notes that are called *re*. _____

c. Count all the notes that are called *la*. _____

d. Count all the notes that are called *do*. _____

What Do You Hear? 1A   Vocal Timbre

Listen to the following vocal timbres. Identify the voice(s) you hear in each listening selection. Circle your answers.

1. male solo   female solo

2. children's chorus   mixed adult chorus

3. solo and chorus   chorus   solo

Assessment 1: Unit 1 (continued)

What Do You Hear? 1B   Form

Listen to "*Ise Oluwa.*" What is the musical form? Circle your answer.

a. call and response   **b.** verse/refrain

What You Can Do

Create a Response

Sing "This Train," on page 27. Then create a simple response part to sing or play at the ends of lines 1, 2, and 4.

Play a Rhythm

Look at the rhythm patterns below.

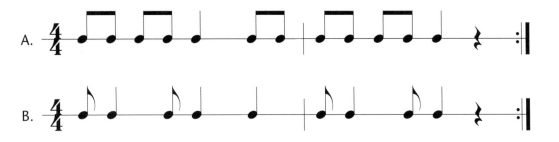

a. As the teacher plays a steady beat on a hand drum, play rhythm A on percussion instruments with the recording of "*Funwa alafia.*"

b. As the teacher plays a steady beat on a hand drum, play rhythm B on percussion instruments with the recording of "*Kokoleoko.*"

Assessment 2: Unit 2

Read these rhythm patterns. Then **play** them on rhythm instruments.

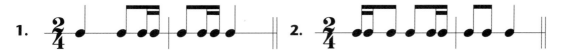

Compose your own "Gold Rush Rhythm" on the staff below and **perform** it with the song "California."

You performed *"Da pacem, Domine"* in F-*do.*

Any song can be transposed, or sung at a higher or lower pitch. **Sing** the version of *"Da pacem, Domine"* below, using hand signs and pitch syllables. Is this version higher or lower than the first version? Where is *do* in this version? Write the pitch syllables below the notes.

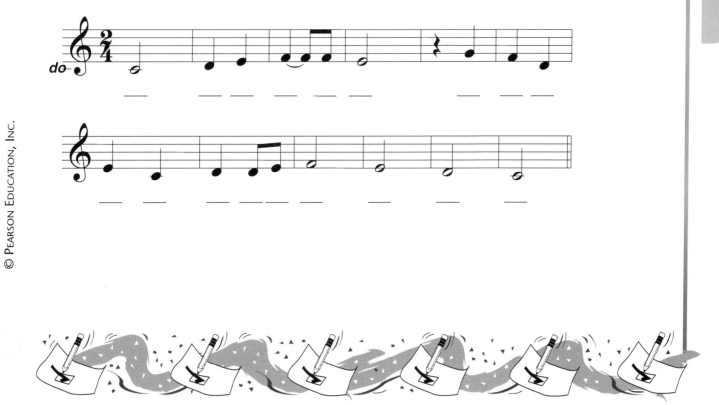

ASSESSMENT 2: UNIT 2 (CONTINUED)

What Do You Know?

1. Match the musical terms on the left with their correct definitions.

a. *crescendo*

_____ The part of a song that repeats, using the same melody and words

b. *decrescendo*

_____ Gradually get louder

c. verse

_____ The section of a song that is sung before the refrain

d. refrain

_____ Gradually get softer

2. Look at the melody for "*Da pacem, Domine,*" page 62. Where is *do*? Notate *do* on the staff. Identify and count the following pitch syllables.

a. Count all notes that are called *mi*. _____

b. Count all notes that are called *fa*. _____

c. Count all notes that are called *re*. _____

ASSESSMENT 2: UNIT 2 (CONTINUED)

● What Do You Hear? 2   Meter

You will hear three songs. Listen and decide whether the music moves in meter in 2 or meter in 3. Circle your answers.

1.   Meter in 2   Meter in 3

2.   Meter in 2   Meter in 3

3.   Meter in 2   Meter in 3

What You Can Do

Choose Your Dynamics

Add *crescendo*, *decrescendo*, and other dynamics to the melody composition you created on page 75. Choose someone to help you perform your piece for the class.

Sing a Melody

Read the notation for "*A la puerta del cielo*," on page 60, using hand signs and pitch syllables. Then sing the song with the words.

Keep a Journal

Keep a music journal. Divide it into three sections.

   a. Vocabulary words

   b. Musical forms

   c. List of favorite songs and listening selections

© PEARSON EDUCATION, INC.

ASSESSMENT

ASSESSMENT 3: UNIT 3

Using a grand staff, **notate** the refrain of "Don't You Hear the Lambs?" on the top staff. On the bottom staff, **notate** an accompaniment using D-major and C-major chords. Use a rhythm pattern in your accompaniment that includes the dotted quarter note and eighth note.

Identify and circle *ti* in each of these patterns. Then **sing** the pattern using hand signs and pitch syllables.

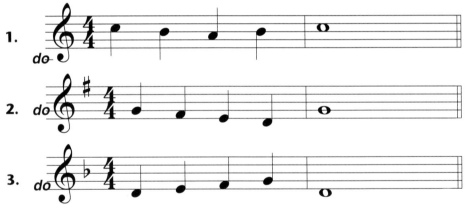

This phrase is from a song in Unit 3. **Sing** the phrase using hand signs and pitch syllables.
Where is *ti* ? Circle that note.
What is the name of the song? _____

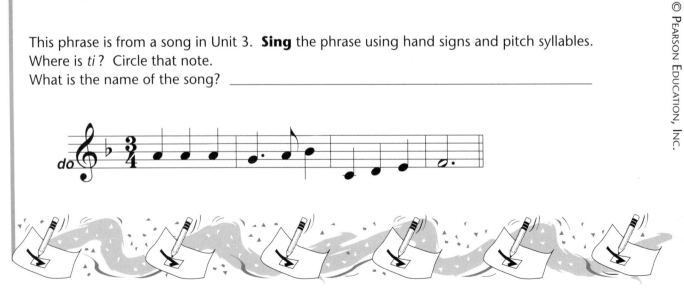

ASSESSMENT 3: UNIT 3 (CONTINUED)

Review, Assess, Perform, Create

What Do You Know?

1. Look at the last four measures of the refrain of "This Land Is Your Land," on page 118, in which *do* is in the first space. Identify and count the following pitch syllables.

    a. Count all the notes called *so*. _____

    b. Count all the notes called *re*. _____

    c. Count all the notes called *ti*. _____

2. Look at the three phrases below. Then answer each question below by placing the letter of the correct phrase in the blank provided.

a.

Josh - ua fought the bat - tle of_____ Jer - i - cho

b.

Sleep, my child, and peace at-tend thee All through the night;

c.

Dun-dai, dun - dai, dun - dai dai, Dun-dai, dun - dai, dun - dai dai.

Which phrase should be performed in a *legato* style? _____

Which phrase should be performed in a *marcato* style? _____

Which phrase should be performed in a *staccato* style? _____

ASSESSMENT

ASSESSMENT 3: UNIT 3 (CONTINUED)

What Do You Hear? 3   Dynamics and Articulation

Listen to four excerpts from *The Stars and Stripes Forever*. Following each excerpt, circle the word that best describes the dynamics or articulation you hear in the music.

1. **a.** *Crescendo*   **b.** *Forte*

2. **a.** *Staccato*   **b.** *Legato*

3. **a.** *Legato*   **b.** *Marcato*

4. **a.** *Pianissimo*   **b.** *Fortissimo*

What You Can Do

Sing and Show Hand Signs

Sing *"Himmel und Erde,"* page 94, using hand signs and pitch syllables. Then sing the song with the lyrics.

Sing and Conduct

Sing "All Through the Night," page 105, and conduct the beat while following the notation. Sing the song using rhythm syllables and then with the lyrics.

Create a Rhythm Pattern

Create a four-measure rhythm pattern in $\frac{3}{4}$ meter using . Be sure to include rests.

Perform your rhythm pattern on an instrument of your choice.

ASSESSMENT 4: UNIT 4

Read these rhythm patterns from "Scotland the Brave" and "Loch Lomond" using rhythm syllables. **Identify** the line in the song that matches each rhythm pattern. Then, clap each pattern as you **sing** the words.

Do and *high do* are shown on the staff below.

Complete the scale by writing in the missing pitch syllables and adding their letter names.

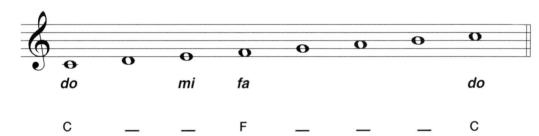

| | do | | mi | fa | | | | do |
| C | — | — | F | — | — | — | C |

Sing the scale using pitch syllables.

ASSESSMENT 4: UNIT 4 (CONTINUED)

Review, Assess, Perform, Create

What Do You Know?

Match the Texture

Look at each type of song that is described on the right. Then match the letter of each picture on the left that best represents the texture. Write your answers in the blanks provided.

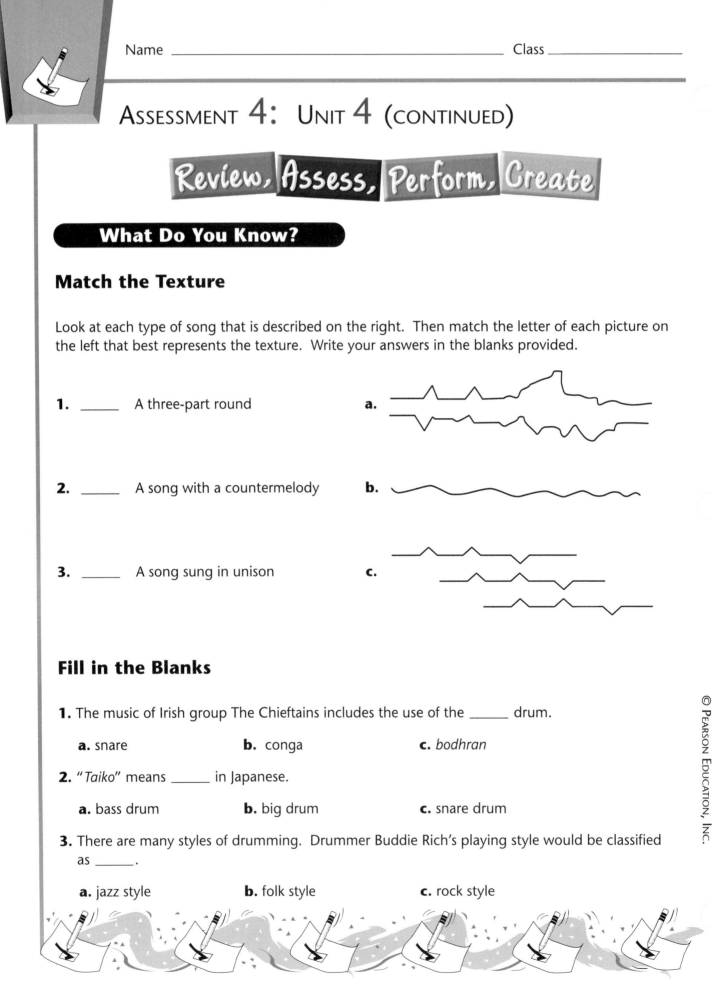

1. _____ A three-part round   a.

2. _____ A song with a countermelody   b.

3. _____ A song sung in unison   c.

Fill in the Blanks

1. The music of Irish group The Chieftains includes the use of the _____ drum.

   a. snare   **b.** conga   **c.** *bodhran*

2. "*Taiko*" means _____ in Japanese.

   a. bass drum   **b.** big drum   **c.** snare drum

3. There are many styles of drumming. Drummer Buddie Rich's playing style would be classified as _____.

   a. jazz style   **b.** folk style   **c.** rock style

ASSESSMENT 4: UNIT 4 (CONTINUED)

 **What Do You Hear? 4**   **Melody Patterns**

Look at the melody patterns below. Each pattern occurs in the listening selection. Place the letter of each pattern in the spaces provided so the order matches what you hear in the recording.

1. _____   4. _____

2. _____   5. _____

3. _____

a.

b.

c.

d.

e.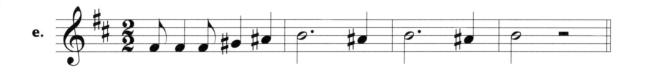

ASSESSMENT 4: UNIT 4 (CONTINUED)

What You Can Do

Listen, Conduct, and Sing

Listen to "Scotland the Brave," page 138, and conduct the beat while following the notation. Sing the song using rhythm syllables and then with the lyrics.

Create a Rondo

Use the two rhythm patterns below, plus a contrasting pattern of your own, to create a rhythm rondo.

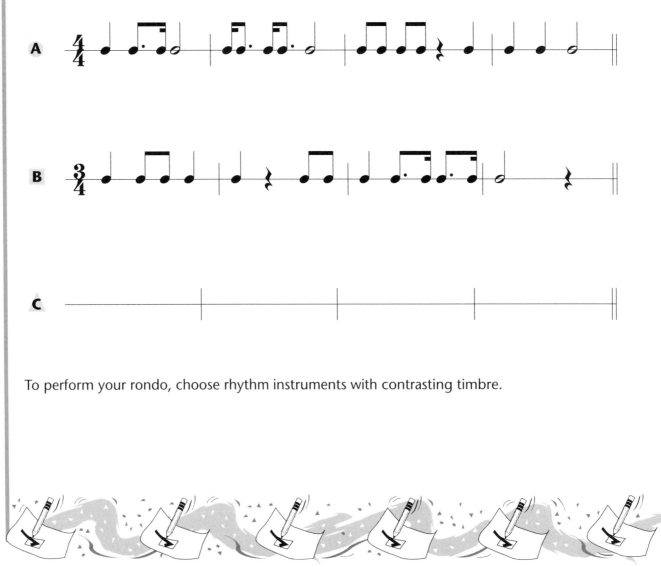

To perform your rondo, choose rhythm instruments with contrasting timbre.

Assessment 5: Unit 5

Clap these patterns in compound meter. Use the patterns to **create** a counter-rhythm. Then **perform** your counter-rhythm as you **sing** "Blow the Wind Southerly."

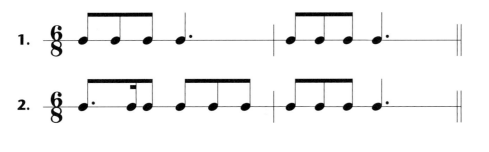

Using pitch syllables, **read** and **sing** each of these minor scales. Which scale is natural minor? Which one is harmonic minor? Write your answers directly above each staff to identify each scale.

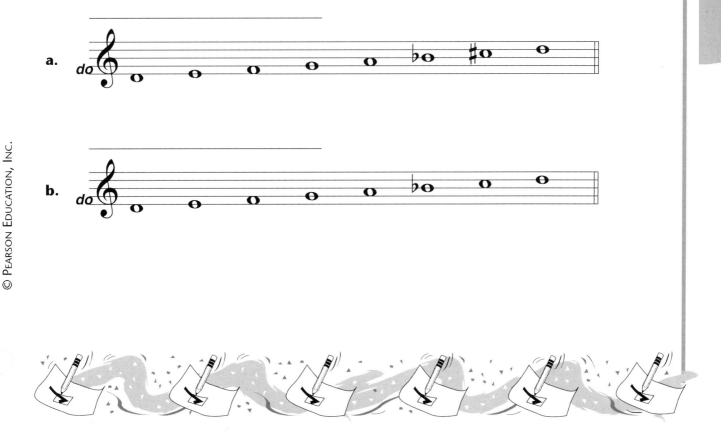

ASSESSMENT 5: UNIT 5 (CONTINUED)

Review, Assess, Perform, Create

What Do You Know?

Fill in the Blanks

1. A mark that indicates to sing or play a note with more emphasis than the other notes is called _____.

   a. a tie   **b.** a slur   **c.** an accent

2. A musical form in which each section is a modification of the initial theme is called _____.

   a. verse and refrain   **b.** solo and chorus   **c.** theme and variations

3. The arrangement of eight tones with a step pattern of whole, half, whole, whole, half, whole, whole, is a _____ scale.

   a. diatonic   **b.** major   **c.** natural minor

What Do You Hear? 5A   Meter

Listen to the following musical excerpts as you conduct the meter. Identify the meter of each selection and circle your answers.

1. $\frac{4}{4}$ meter $\frac{6}{8}$ meter

2. $\frac{6}{8}$ meter $\frac{2}{4}$ meter

3. $\frac{6}{8}$ meter $\frac{4}{4}$ meter

What Do You Hear? 5B   Timbre

Listen to the following musical excerpts of string instruments and identify whether the instrument you hear is plucked, bowed, or struck. Circle your answers.

1.   plucked   bowed   struck

2.   plucked   bowed   struck

3.   plucked   bowed   struck

Assessment 5: Unit 5 (continued)

What You Can Do

Play Chords

As the group sings "Mango Walk," on page 200, accompany the singers on Autoharp or keyboard. Be sure to play the I and V_7 chords at the appropriate time.

Create a Melodic Poem

Read the poem "Who Has Seen the Wind?" by Christina Rossetti on page 207.

Work together in two groups to create a melody. Group 1 should create a melody in C major, ending on C, to accompany lines 1–4 of the poem. Group 2 should create a melody in A minor, ending on A, to accompany lines 5–8 of the poem.

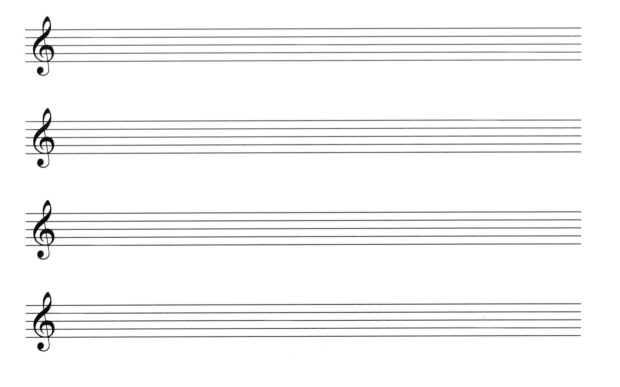

Play and sing your melodies for the other group. Review each performance. Which melody did you like best and why? How could you improve it?

ASSESSMENT 6: UNIT 6

Play or **sing** the melody below.

Identify the song it's from. _____

Now **notate** this melody using augmentation.

Now **notate** this melody using diminution.

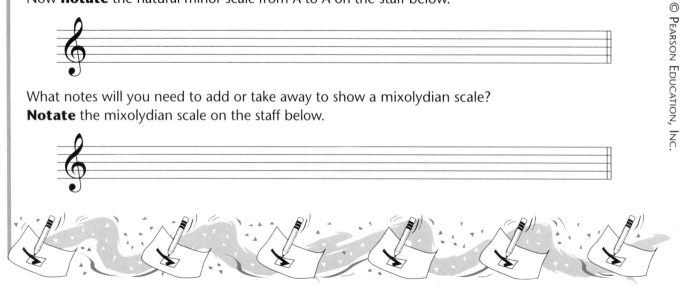

The C-major scale is notated below.

Now **notate** the natural minor scale from A to A on the staff below.

What notes will you need to add or take away to show a mixolydian scale?
Notate the mixolydian scale on the staff below.

ASSESSMENT 6: UNIT 6 (CONTINUED)

Review, Assess, Perform, Create

What Do You Know?

1. Which of the following are expressive qualities? _____
   a. form   **b.** tempo   **c.** dynamics

2. Meter in 5 means _____.
   a. the music has   **b.** there is no   **c.** there are five beats
   only five measures   such meter   in a measure

3. In music, blues is an expression, a feeling, and a _____.
   a. meter   **b.** form   **c.** verse

4. The dorian scale begins on _____.
   a. *do*   **b.** *la*   **c.** *re*

What Do You Hear? 6A **Tonality**

Listen to each of the following excerpts to identify its tonality. Circle your answers.

1. major   minor

2. major   minor

3. major   minor

4. major   minor

What Do You Hear? 6B **Timbre**

Listen to the following excerpts. Circle the name of the instrument you hear in each excerpt.

1. harpsichord   piano   synthesizer

2. harpsichord   piano   synthesizer

3. harpsichord   piano   synthesizer

ASSESSMENT 6: UNIT 6 (CONTINUED)

What You Can Do

Create a 12-bar Blues Song

• Compose your own 12-bar blues song (see the form of "Good Mornin', Blues," page 224, for an example).

• Notate your melody in the key of C.

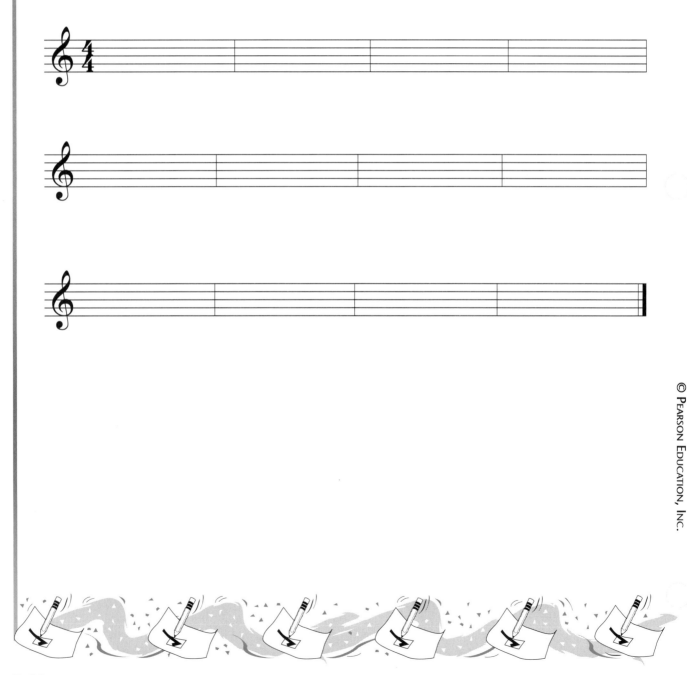

ASSESSMENT 6: UNIT 6 (CONTINUED)

Show the Meter

Listen to *Ali Pasha* and *Take Five.* Perform steady-beat movements that reflect the accent pattern of the meter in 5.

Sing in Harmony

Practice singing in two- and three-part harmony by reviewing these songs in Unit 6.

"Linstead Market," page 241

"Ev'ry Time I Feel the Spirit," page 242

"*Kum ba yah*," page 244

Work in small groups and

- Choose one song.

- Decide who will sing the melody and who will sing the harmony parts.

- Practice each part.

- Perform your song for the teacher and the other groups.

- Discuss how well each group was able to sing in two or three parts. Then offer suggestions that will help each group improve its performance.

Assessment: Introduction

Introduction for the Music Teacher

Checklists

Checklists are provided for performance skills (singing, playing instruments, reading, improvising, moving) and non-performance skills (composing/arranging/notating, listening). Have individual students demonstrate each of the items on the checklists. Guide the students in selecting music and tasks that will permit them to meet all of the goals outlined in the checklists.

You may consider assembling small ensembles in which students with different skill levels all perform a given piece together, but with students playing parts that are appropriate for their various skill levels. When reviewing students' work, continue to refer to the items on the checklists and point out ways their work does or does not meet each of the criteria. For students who do not perform as well as they are capable, provide opportunities to perform small sections of their pieces again. Have the students pay attention to one or two specific points that will improve their work. In this way, assessment becomes an important and contributing part of the learning process.

Rubrics

The rubrics are designed to be used together with the checklists. The goal of performance skills is for all students to perform well, regardless of the difficulty of the material they perform. The goal of non-performance skills is for all students to demonstrate competence, regardless of the difficulty of the composing, arranging, and listening tasks that they are assigned. Of course, some items on the checklists are more important than others, but all of them work together to create successful, expressive music performances, compositions, or informed listening experiences. If you wish to summarize your evaluations of the students' performances or work in a way that allows you to place each student or small group on a graded scale, you may use the rubrics for describing their performances or work.

ASSESSMENT: PERFORMANCE SKILLS

Singing

Checklist for Singing
❑ Posture is upright and relaxed.
❑ Jaw and mouth are relaxed and open.
❑ Breath is inhaled with natural, relaxed expansion of the body.
❑ Tone is free, open, and even throughout range.
❑ Singing is accurate and in tune.
❑ Rhythm is precise and sung with inflection.
❑ Diction is clear (all words are understood).
❑ Volume level is balanced with other members of the ensemble.
❑ Dynamic and rhythmic variations are used to create expressive effects.

Rubric for Singing
❑ **Fluent** The student sings with fluency and ease. There are few errors. All items on the checklist are consistently demonstrated. The performance is confident, beautiful, and expressive.

❑ **Competent** The student sings with relative ease, but several errors or hesitations are present. Most items on the checklist are consistently demonstrated. The performance is confident and expressive.

❑ **More Practice Needed** The student has difficulty performing evenly and in time. Hesitations and errors are clearly evident. Only some of the checklist items are demonstrated. The performance does not convey the expressive intent of the piece performed.

ASSESSMENT

Assessment: Performance Skills

Playing Instruments

Checklist for Playing Instruments
- ❏ Posture is upright and relaxed.
- ❏ Instruments, sticks, and mallets (when used) are held loosely and comfortably.
- ❏ Arms, hands, and fingers move easily (no tension evident).
- ❏ Playing motion is efficient and smooth.
- ❏ Instrument tone is open, resonant, and even.
- ❏ Notes are performed accurately and in tune.
- ❏ Rhythm is accurate and precise.
- ❏ Tempo is steady and even.
- ❏ Volume level is balanced with other members of the ensemble.
- ❏ Dynamic and rhythmic variations are used to create expressive effects.

Rubric for Playing Instruments

❏ **Fluent** The student plays with fluency and ease. There are few errors. All items on the checklist are consistently demonstrated. The performance is confident, beautiful, and expressive.

❏ **Competent** The student plays with relative ease, but several errors or hesitations are present. Most items on the checklist are consistently demonstrated. The performance is confident and expressive.

❏ **More Practice Needed** The student has difficulty performing evenly and in time. Hesitations and errors are clearly evident. Only some of the checklist items are demonstrated. The performance does not convey the expressive intent of the piece performed.

ASSESSMENT: PERFORMANCE SKILLS

Reading

*Checklist for Reading

*❑ Selects appropriate tempo at which to perform unfamiliar music.

*❑ Identifies passages that are not immediately interpretable or technically difficult.

❑ Rehearses difficult or unfamiliar elements in isolation.

❑ Pitches are performed accurately.

❑ Rhythm is accurate and precise.

❑ Rhythm is performed with appropriate inflection.

❑ Style of articulation (if applicable) is accurate and consistent.

❑ Dynamic levels are accurate.

❑ Tempo is steady and even when appropriate.

❑ Rhythmic and dynamic variations are used to create expressive effects.

* Refer to tasks involved in learning unfamiliar music.

Rubric for Reading

❑ Fluent The student reads with fluency and ease. There are few errors. All items on the checklist are consistently demonstrated. The performance is confident, beautiful, and expressive.

❑ Competent The student reads with relative ease, but several errors or hesitations are present. Most items on the checklist are consistently demonstrated. The performance is confident and expressive.

❑ More Practice Needed The student has difficulty performing evenly and in time. Hesitations and errors are clearly evident. Only some of the checklist items are demonstrated. The performance does not convey the expressive intent of the piece performed.

ASSESSMENT: PERFORMANCE SKILLS

Moving and Improvising

Checklist for Moving
❑ Weight of the body is balanced and secure.
❑ Limbs move easily and without unnecessary tension.
❑ Movements depict the style of music (for example, rhythm, articulation).
❑ Movements are coordinated with the pulse of the music (if applicable).
❑ Changes in movements appropriately mirror changes in the music.
❑ Sizes and distances of movements are appropriate for the occasion and location (for example, on a dance floor, in a circle with classmates, or seated in a chair).

Checklist for Improvising
❑ Notes are grouped in discernible phrases.
❑ Repetition of melodic motives is used to extend and elaborate phrases.
❑ Individual phrases are unified by consistency and continuity.
❑ Phrases are organized with clear, balanced antecedents and consequents.
❑ Harmonic motion (when harmony is present) is logical.
❑ Dynamic and rhythmic variations are used to create expressive effects.
❑ Musical effects are consistent with the improviser's intent.

Rubric for Moving and Improvising
❑ **Fluent** The student moves or improvises with fluency and ease. There are few errors. All items on the checklist are consistently demonstrated. The performance is confident, beautiful, and expressive.

❑ **Competent** The student moves or improvises with relative ease, but several errors or hesitations are present. Most items on the checklist are consistently demonstrated. The performance is confident and expressive.

❑ **More Practice Needed** The student has difficulty performing evenly and in time. Hesitations and errors are clearly evident. Only some of the checklist items are demonstrated. The performance does not convey the expressive intent of the piece performed.

Assessment: Non-Performance Skills

Composing/Arranging/Notating

Checklist for Composing/Arranging/Notating
❑ Instrument timbres and voice parts are combined effectively.
❑ Notes are grouped in phrases.
❑ Repetition of melodic motives is used to extend and elaborate phrases.
❑ Individual phrases are unified by consistency and continuity.
❑ Phrases are organized with clear, balanced antecedents and consequents.
❑ Harmonic motion (when harmony is present) is logical.
❑ Part-writing (if applicable) follows the conventions of the style of composition.
❑ Dynamic and rhythmic variations are used to create expressive effects.
❑ Musical effects are consistent with the intent of the composer or arranger.
❑ Musical sounds are accurately transcribed using formal, informal, or invented notation.
❑ Notation is clear and readable by others.

Rubric for Composing/Arranging/Notating
❑ **Fluent** The composition or arrangement is expressive, beautiful, and consistent with the intent of the composer or arranger. All items on the checklist are consistently demonstrated.

❑ **Competent** The composition or arrangement is well organized and consistent with the intent of the composer or arranger. Most items on the checklist are consistently demonstrated.

❑ **More Practice Needed** The composition or arrangement is somewhat organized and may not be consistent with the intent of the composer or arranger. Only some of the checklist items are demonstrated.

ASSESSMENT

ASSESSMENT: NON-PERFORMANCE SKILLS

Listening

Checklist for Listening

The first four items on this checklist pertain to behavior while listening; the remaining four pertain to auditory discriminations explained after listening.

❏ Remains quiet (when appropriate) while listening to live or recorded music.
❏ Remains stationary (when appropriate) while listening to live or recorded music.
❏ Moves appropriately while listening to music (for example, tapping to the beat, dancing) in social settings where movement is appropriate.
❏ Acknowledges performers with applause (when appropriate).
❏ Describes the timbres of musical tones and labels instruments and voice parts.
❏ Describes the formal organization of sounds (for example, the use of repetition, melodic contour, motivic development).
❏ Describes the emotional effects that the music elicits from self and others.
❏ Describes possible functions of the music in cultural contexts.

Rubric for Listening Discrimination

❏ **Fluent** All aspects of the music are accurately described, and the observations about the music are informative and interesting. All items on the checklist are consistently demonstrated.

❏ **Competent** Most aspects of the music are accurately described, and the observations about the music are informative. Most items on the checklist are consistently demonstrated.

❏ **More Practice Needed** Aspects of the music are described, but some important information is inaccurate or omitted. Only some of the checklist items are demonstrated.

ASSESSMENT ANSWER KEY

Unit 1 (Pages B-2 to B-4)

Show What You Know! (Rhythm)
Patterns b and d use syncopation

What Do You Know?
1. **f.** *forte* (loud)
   - **a.** *piano* (soft)
   - **e.** *pianissimo* (medium soft)
   - **c.** *fortissimo* (very loud)
   - **b.** *mezzo forte* (very soft)
   - **d.** *mezzo piano* (medium loud)
2. **a.** *so* = thirteen
   - **b.** *re* = six
   - **c.** *la* = five
   - **d.** *do* = sixteen

What Do You Hear? 1A
1. male solo
2. children's chorus
3. solo and chorus

What Do You Hear? 1B
   - **a.** call and response

Unit 2 (Pages B-5 to B-7)

Show What You Know! (Melody)
This version is lower than the first; *do* = C;
do-re-mi-fa-fa-mi-so-fa-re-mi-do-re-re-mi-fa-mi-re-do

What Do You Know?
1. **d.** refrain
   - **a.** *crescendo*
   - **c.** verse
   - **b.** *decrescendo*
2. **a.** *mi* = five
   - **b.** *fa* = four
   - **c.** *re* = five

What Do You Hear? 2
1. meter in 3
2. meter in 3
3. meter in 2

Unit 3 (Pages B-8 to B-10)

Show What You Know! (Melody)
1. *ti* = B; *do-ti-la-ti-do*
2. *ti* = F; *do-ti-la-so-do*
3. *ti* = E; *la-ti-do-re-do*
4. **a.** *ti* = E; *mi-mi-mi-re-mi-fa-so-la-ti-do*
   - **b.** "Himmel und Erde"

What Do You Know?
1. **a.** *so* = one
   - **b.** *re* = four
   - **c.** *ti* = two
2. *legato* = **b.**
   marcato = **c.**
   staccato = **a.**

What Do You Hear? 3
1. **a.** *Crescendo*
2. **b.** *Legato*
3. **b.** *Marcato*
4. **b.** *Fortissimo*

Unit 4 (Pages B-11 to B-14)

Show What You Know! (Rhythm)
Kodály-based rhythm syllables:
   - **a.** *ta teem-ri ti-ti ti-ti ta teem-ri ti-ti ti-ti*
   - **b.** *ti-ti ri-teem re-teem ta ti-ti ta-a ta*

Show What You Know! (Melody)
D = *re*; E = *mi*; F = *fa*; G = *so*; A = *la*; B = *ti*

What Do You Know?
Match the Texture
1. **c.** a three-part round
2. **a.** a song with a countermelody
3. **b.** a song sung in unison
Fill in the Blanks
1. **c.** *bodhran*
2. **b.** big drum
3. **a.** jazz style

What Do You Hear? 4
1. c.
2. a.
3. d.
4. e.
5. b.

ASSESSMENT

Assessment Answer Key (continued)

Unit 5 (Pages B-15 to B-17)

Show What You Know! (Melody)

    a. *la-ti-do-re-mi-fa-si-la;* harmonic minor

    b. *la-ti-do-re-mi-fa-so-la;* natural minor

What Do You Know?

    1. c. an accent

    2. c. theme and variations

    3. c. natural minor

What Do You Hear? 5A

    1. $\frac{4}{4}$ meter

    2. $\frac{2}{4}$ meter

    3. $\frac{6}{8}$ meter

What Do You Hear? 5B

    1. plucked

    2. bowed

    3. struck

Unit 6 (Pages B-18 to B-21)

Show What You Know! (Rhythm)

    "Mango Walk"

What Do You Know?

    1. b. tempo and **c.** dynamics

    2. c. there are five beats in a measure

    3. b. form

    4. c. *re*

What Do You Hear? 6A

    1. major

    2. minor

    3. minor

    4. major

What Do You Hear? 6B

    1. piano

    2. harpsichord

    3. synthesizer

GRAPHIC ORGANIZERS

Table of Contents

Comparison C-2

Information Organizer Chart C-3

KWHL Chart C-4

Semantic Feature Analysis C-5

Story Map C-7

Venn Diagram C-8

GRAPHIC ORGANIZER

GRAPHIC ORGANIZER 1

Comparison

Alike	Different

GRAPHIC ORGANIZER 2

Information Organizer Chart

GRAPHIC ORGANIZER 3

KWHL Chart

What I know	
What I want to know	
How I will learn this	
What I learned	

GRAPHIC ORGANIZER 4

Semantic Feature Analysis

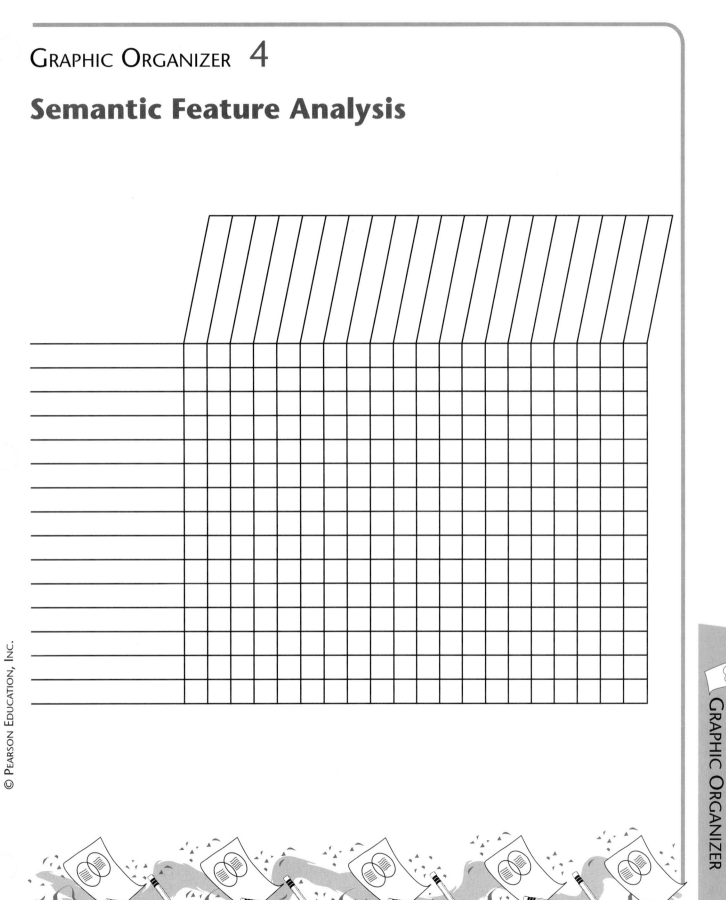

GRAPHIC ORGANIZER 5

Semantic Map

GRAPHIC ORGANIZER 6

Story Map

Title: _____

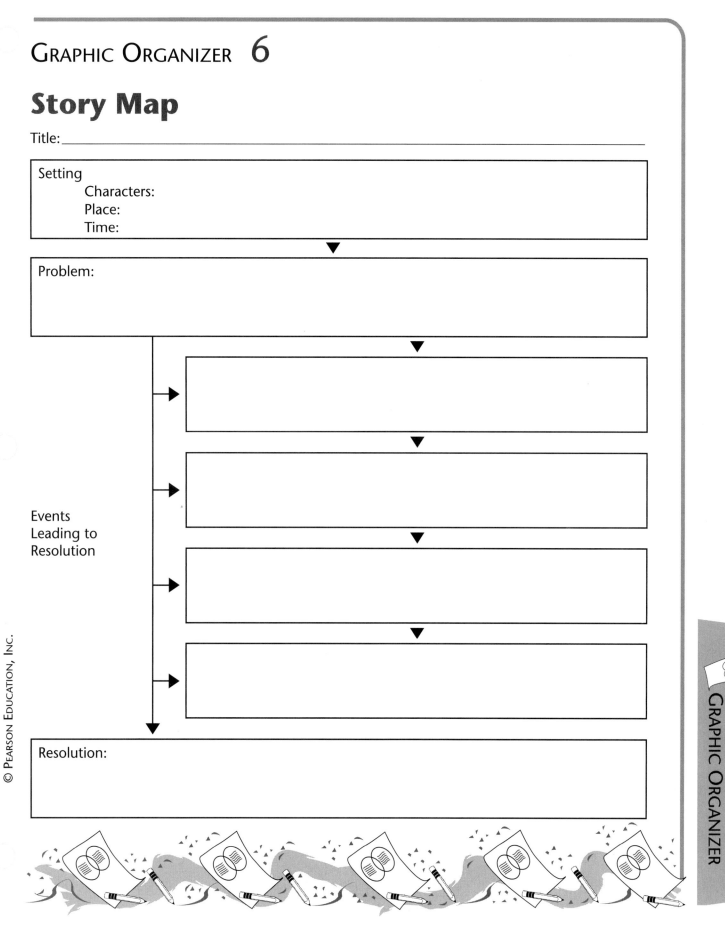

Setting
     Characters:
     Place:
     Time:

▼

Problem:

▼

▼

Events
Leading to
Resolution

▼

▼

Resolution:

GRAPHIC ORGANIZER

GRAPHIC ORGANIZER 7

Venn Diagram

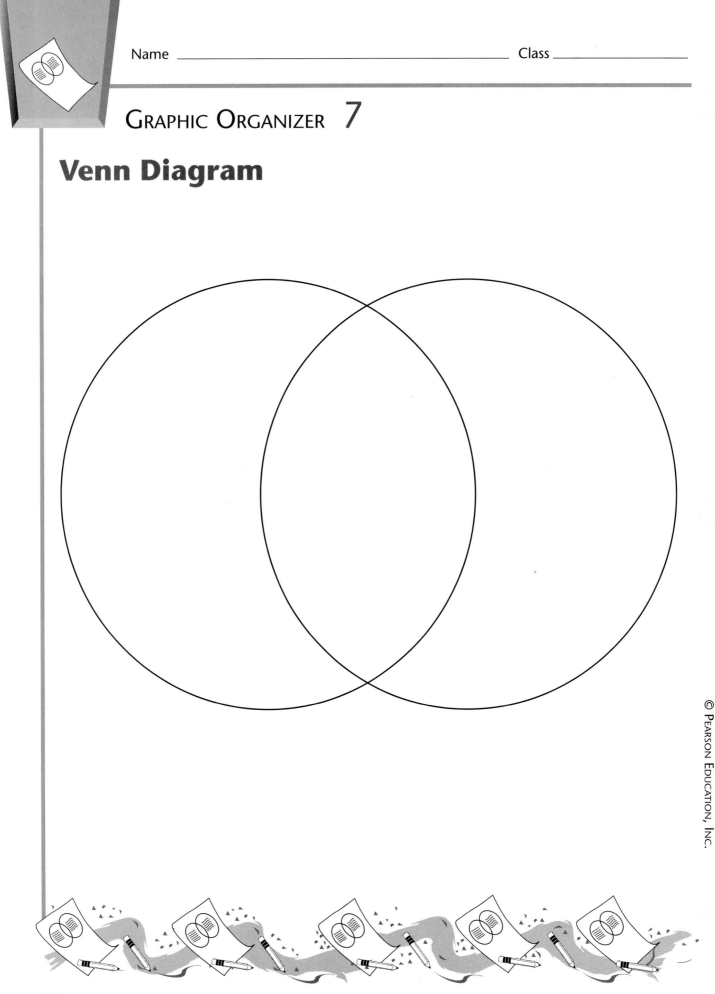

MUSIC READING WORKSHEETS
Table of Contents

UNIT 1

Clap and Count—*Morning Comes Early* D-2

Reading the Pentatonic Scale D-3

Singing Secrets D-4

UNIT 2

Name That Rhythm! D-5

Where's *fa?*—*A la puerta del cielo* (At the Gate of Heaven) D-6

UNIT 3

Writing Rhythms D-9

A New Dotted Rhythm D-11

Ti Time D-12

Countermelodies D-14

UNIT 4

Tied Up in Notes—*Wabash Cannon Ball* D-16

Fitting the Rhythm—*Loch Lomond* D-18

The Major Diatonic Scale D-20

Melodic Sequence D-22

UNIT 5

What's the Meter?—*Las estrellitas del cielo* (Stars of the Heavens) D-23

The Natural Minor Scale D-24

The Harmonic Minor Scale/Another Minor Scale D-26

UNIT 6

A New Rhythm D-28

Augmenting and Diminishing Rhythms D-30

A New Scale; a New Mode D-31

A Minor Mode D-32

Curwen Hand Signs **D-33**

MUSIC READING WORKSHEET 1

Clap and Count

Morning Comes Early

Slovak Folk Song

Read, clap, and say the rhythm patterns below.

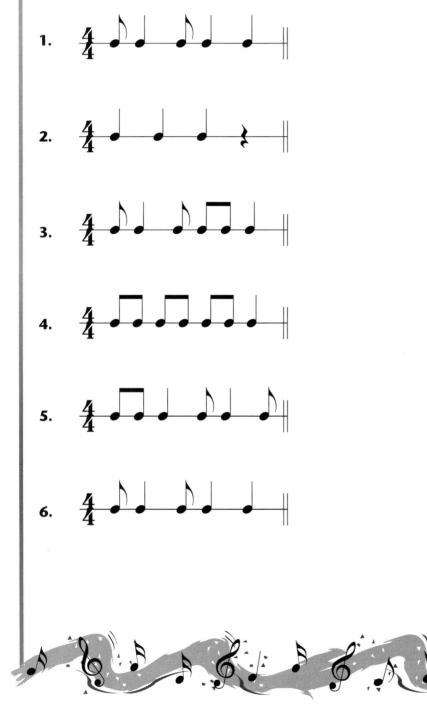

1.

2.

3.

4.

5.

6.

MUSIC READING WORKSHEET 2

Reading the Pentatonic Scale

◯

la

so

mi
re
do

◯

◯

Read a pentatonic scale from the pitch ladder. Where are the steps in the scale? Where are the skips?

Using hand signs, sing the pentatonic scale going up and then back down again.

Now add the missing pitch syllables in the circles.

Read the extended pentatonic scale from the staff. The *do* symbol will help you find your way around. Add the missing pitch syllables in the spaces below.

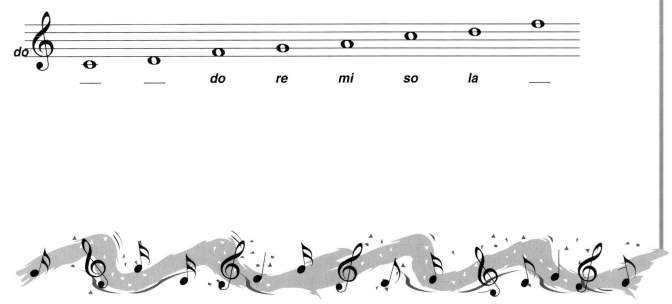

do   ___   ___   do   re   mi   so   la   ___

Music Reading Worksheet 3

Singing Secrets

Play a game by reading and singing these melody patterns.

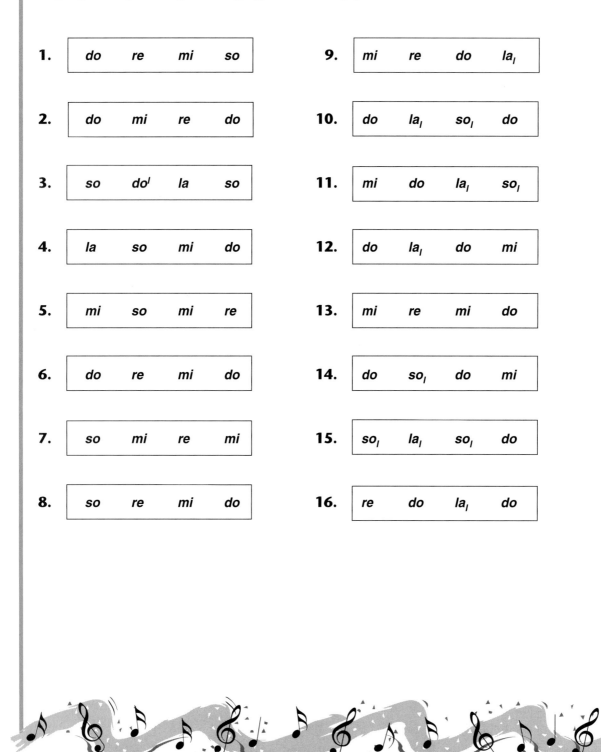

| 1. | do | re | mi | so |

| 2. | do | mi | re | do |

| 3. | so | do^l | la | so |

| 4. | la | so | mi | do |

| 5. | mi | so | mi | re |

| 6. | do | re | mi | do |

| 7. | so | mi | re | mi |

| 8. | so | re | mi | do |

| 9. | mi | re | do | la$_l$ |

| 10. | do | la$_l$ | so$_l$ | do |

| 11. | mi | do | la$_l$ | so$_l$ |

| 12. | do | la$_l$ | do | mi |

| 13. | mi | re | mi | do |

| 14. | do | so$_l$ | do | mi |

| 15. | so$_l$ | la$_l$ | so$_l$ | do |

| 16. | re | do | la$_l$ | do |

MUSIC READING WORKSHEET 4

Name That Rhythm!

Write rhythm syllables for each rhythm below.

Music Reading Worksheet 5

Where's *fa*?

Read and sing this countermelody to *"A la puerta del cielo."*

A la puerta del cielo (At the Gate of Heaven)

Folk Song from Spain

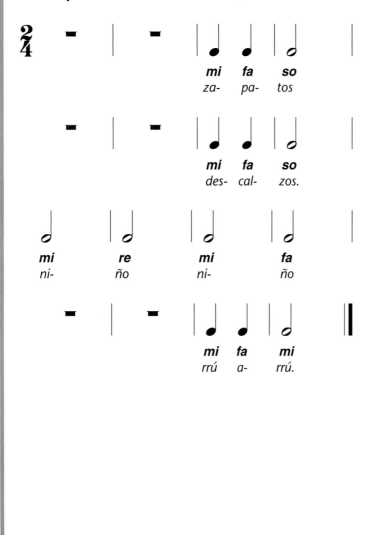

MUSIC READING WORKSHEET 5 (CONTINUED)

Now read the countermelody from staff notation.

MUSIC READING WORKSHEET 5 (CONTINUED)

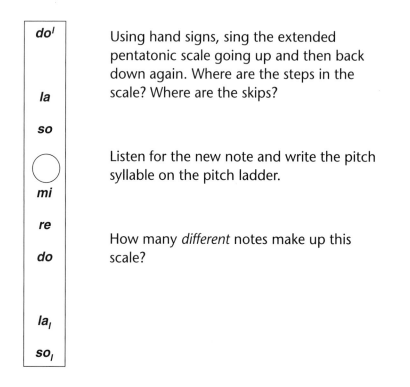

Using hand signs, sing the extended pentatonic scale going up and then back down again. Where are the steps in the scale? Where are the skips?

Listen for the new note and write the pitch syllable on the pitch ladder.

How many *different* notes make up this scale?

Now read the hexachordal scale from the staff. The *do* symbol will help you find your way around. Add the missing pitch syllable in the space below.

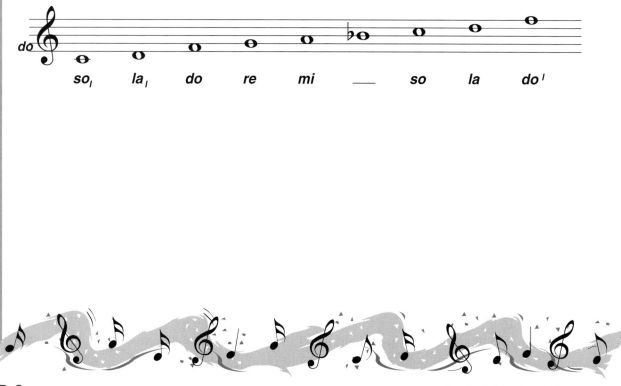

MUSIC READING WORKSHEET 6

Writing Rhythms

Keep a steady beat while you say the words below.

Now clap this pattern as you say the words. Is the pattern the same or different?

Use the tie to transform the rhythm above into the rhythm of the words. Where will you draw the tie?

That's one way to write the rhythm, but there is another, easier way!

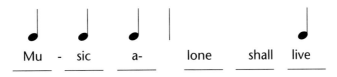

Can you use the new rhythmic figure to complete the phrase?

© PEARSON EDUCATION, INC.

MUSIC READING WORKSHEET 6 (CONTINUED)

Clap and count these phrases, using rhythm syllables. Then perform them as a counter-rhythm to "Music Alone Shall Live." Compose words to the counter-rhythm. Then compose a pentatonic tune for your new text.

Grade 5, Teacher Edition, page 94

MUSIC READING WORKSHEET 7

A New Dotted Rhythm

Use the tie to make the pattern fit the rhythm of the words of "Don't You Hear the Lambs?"

oth - er _____ green _____

You can use an eighth note and a dotted quarter note to show the same rhythm in a different way.

Fill in the missing rhythm using the new dotted rhythm.

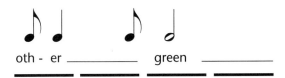

oth - er _____ green _____

MUSIC READING WORKSHEET 8

Ti Time

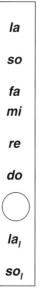

la
so
fa
mi
re
do
○
la₍ₗ₎
so₍ₗ₎

Sing these notes from bottom to top, using hand signs.
Your teacher will sing the missing note. Can you describe it?
Where are the steps in this scale? Where are the half steps?

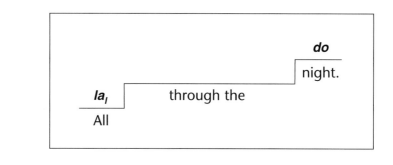

do
night.

la₍ₗ₎   through the

All

The note between *la*₍ₗ₎ and *do* is called *ti*₍ₗ₎. Since it is below *do*, it is called *low ti*. Fill in the missing pitch syllable on the pitch ladder and in the phrase above.

Now find the place for *ti*₍ₗ₎ on the staff, and fill in the missing note.

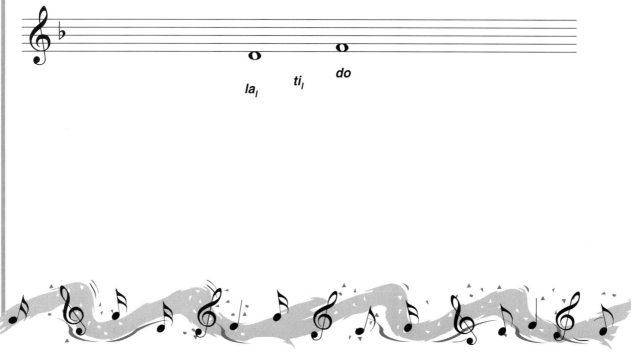

la₍ₗ₎   *ti*₍ₗ₎   *do*

MUSIC READING WORKSHEET 8 (CONTINUED)

Listen as your teacher plays six rhythm patterns. Notate the rhythms in the boxes below.

Then listen as your teacher sings each pattern. Write the pitch syllables under each pattern.

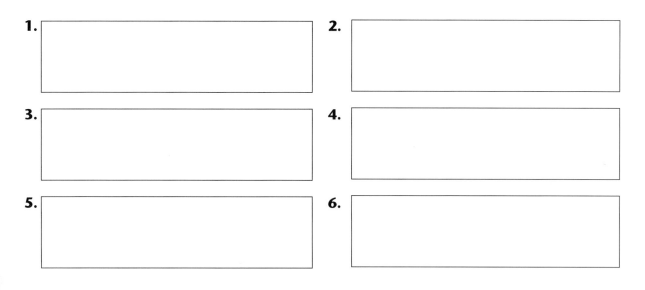

Notate each of the six patterns on the staves below.

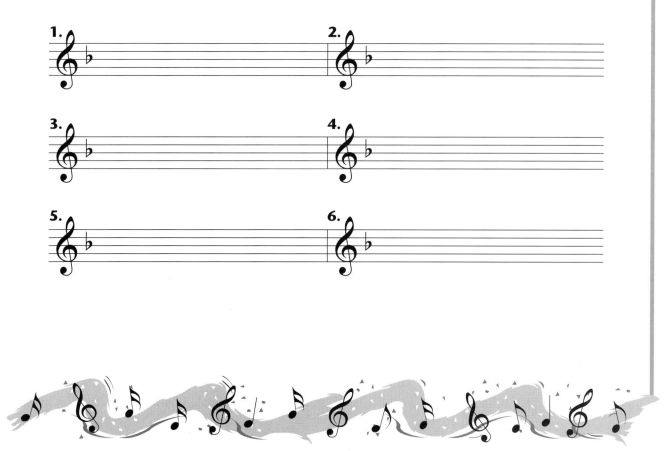

MUSIC READING WORKSHEET 9

Countermelodies

Read and sing this exercise using hand signs and pitch syllables.

Write the pitch set from the lowest note to the highest, and circle the final note.

_____   _____   _____   _____   _____

© PEARSON EDUCATION, INC.

MUSIC READING WORKSHEET 9 (CONTINUED)

Notate the melody from page 106 in your book on the staff. Then create and notate your own countermelody for the melody on page 107, using the rhythm above the staff.

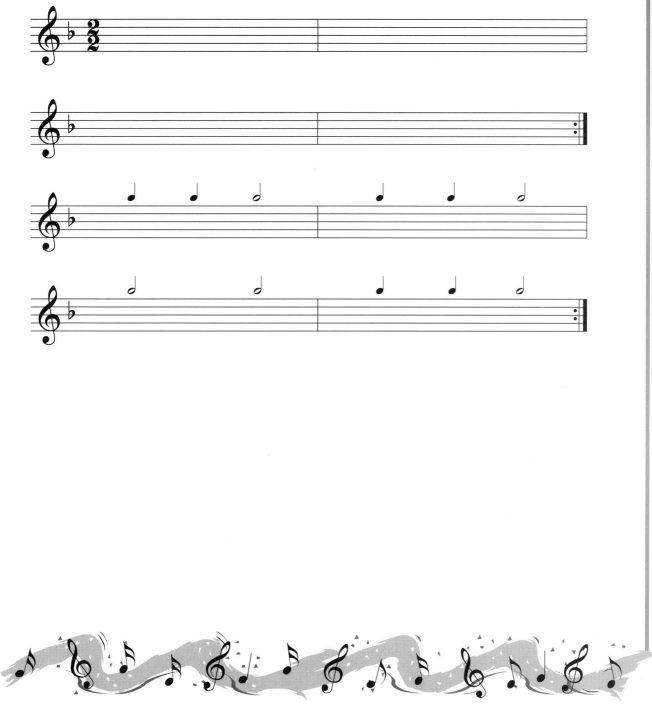

Music Reading Worksheet 10

Tied Up in Notes

Look carefully at the first line of "Wabash Cannon Ball." How do the words fit with the counter-rhythm? Which beats are different? Use the tie to make the rhythm fit the words.

Wabash Cannon Ball

Traditional

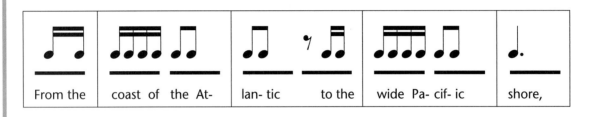

From the | coast of the At- | lan- tic   to the | wide Pa- cif- ic | shore,

You can use a dotted eighth note and sixteenth note to show the same rhythm in a different way.

Grade 5, Teacher Edition, page 136

MUSIC READING WORKSHEET 10 (CONTINUED)

Read, clap, and count the rhythm in the boxes below. Try to tap the rhythm as you sing the song.

Now create a different rhythm for the refrain. Use any of the rhythms you know.

MUSIC READING WORKSHEET 11

Fitting the Rhythm

Look carefully at the last line of "Loch Lomond." How do the words fit with the rhythm? Which beats are different? Use the tie to make the rhythm fit the words.

Loch Lomond

Folk Song from Scotland

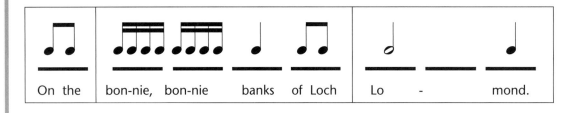

| On the | bon-nie, bon-nie | banks of Loch | Lo - mond. |

You can use a sixteenth note and dotted eighth note to show the same rhythm in a different way.

Grade 5, Teacher Edition, page 138

MUSIC READING WORKSHEET 11 (CONTINUED)

Create a counter-rhythm for the refrain of "Scotland the Brave" or "Loch Lomond." Use any of the rhythms you know to create four-beat patterns. Once you have written your new piece, play it on a percussion instrument as an accompaniment for the songs.

READING WORKSHEETS

MUSIC READING WORKSHEET 12

The Major Diatonic Scale

Sing up and down the scale using pitch syllables, then hand signs. Draw a circle around the notes that are a half step apart.

Fill in the whole and half steps, and draw a circle around the half steps.

Sing the scale again using whole and half steps.

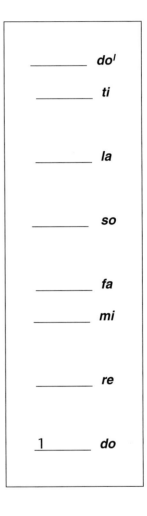

_____ *do¹*

_____ *ti*

_____ *la*

_____ *so*

_____ *fa*

_____ *mi*

_____ *re*

1 _____ *do*

MUSIC READING WORKSHEET 12 (CONTINUED)

Read and sing the scale using pitch syllables and hand signs. Then sing the letter names.

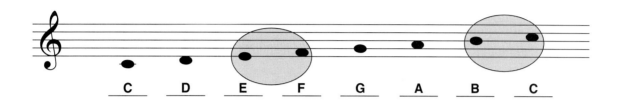

C D E F G A B C

When C is *do,* the pattern of whole and half steps falls into place naturally because the steps between the notes E and F and B and C are half steps. But when other notes are *do,* the pattern must be created using flatted or sharped notes. Figure out the notes you will need for each of the major scales below, and then write them on the staff. (Hint: Look at the key signature. What does it tell you?)

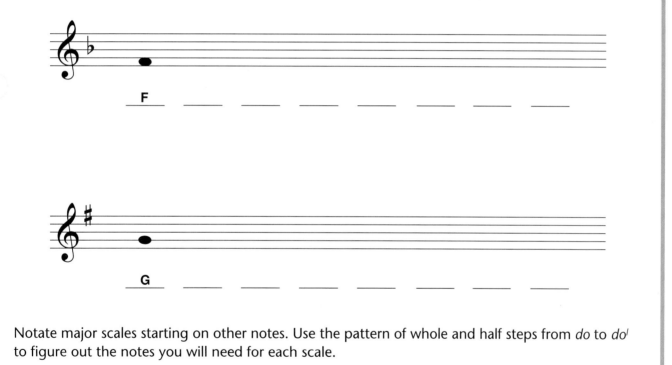

F

G

Notate major scales starting on other notes. Use the pattern of whole and half steps from *do* to *do*ˡ to figure out the notes you will need for each scale.

MUSIC READING WORKSHEET 13

Melodic Sequence

Read the melodic sequence in the first measure of each line. Then notate the pattern in measures 2–4, starting on the notes given. Sing or play each one.

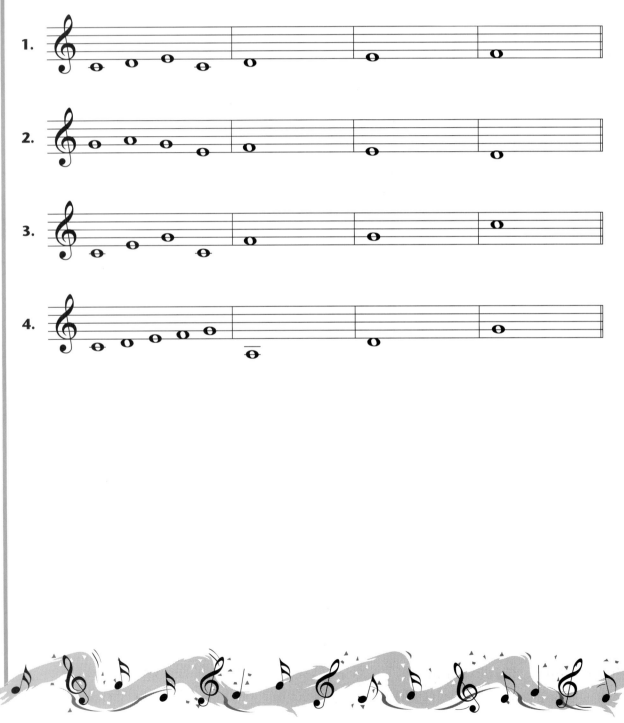

Name _____   Class _____

MUSIC READING WORKSHEET 14

What's the Meter?

Sing this song, and darken the heavy beats. Then draw in bar lines before each heavy beat.
(You don't need one at the beginning.)

Las estrellitas del cielo (Stars of the Heavens)

Folk Song from Spain

Las	es -	tre -	lli-	tas	del	cie		- lo,

| Bri- | llan | con | su | luz | de | pla | | - ta. |

| San- | tia- | go | las | fué | sem- | bran | | - do |

| Con | sus | es- | pue | -las | de | pla | | - ta. |

Now sing *"Las estrellitas del cielo"* while tapping each pattern below. Which pattern feels more comfortable with the song?

Simple Meter
subdivides easily into twos

Compound Meter
subdivides easily into threes

Circle the meter that fits the song.

Name _____   Class _____

MUSIC READING WORKSHEET 15

The Natural Minor Scale

Sing this scale from bottom to top and back down again, using pitch syllables and hand signs.

Draw a circle around the notes which are a half step apart.

Sing the scale again using numbers.

la
so
fa
mi
re
do
ti,
la,

Now read the natural minor scale from the staff. The *do* symbol will help you find your way around.

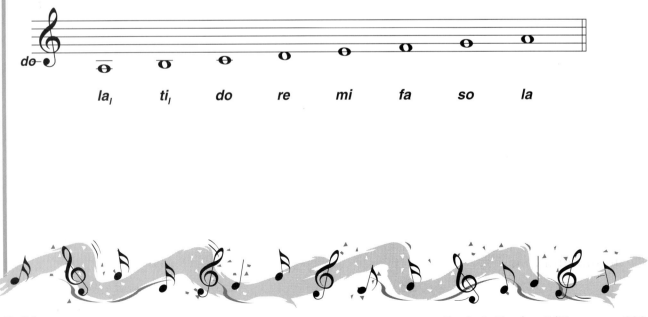

la, *ti,* *do* *re* *mi* *fa* *so* *la*

MUSIC READING WORKSHEET 15 (CONTINUED)

Write the scale degree numbers of the natural minor scale, from *la,* to *la* below the scale. Sing the scale using pitch syllables and hand signs. Then write the pattern of whole and half steps above the scale.

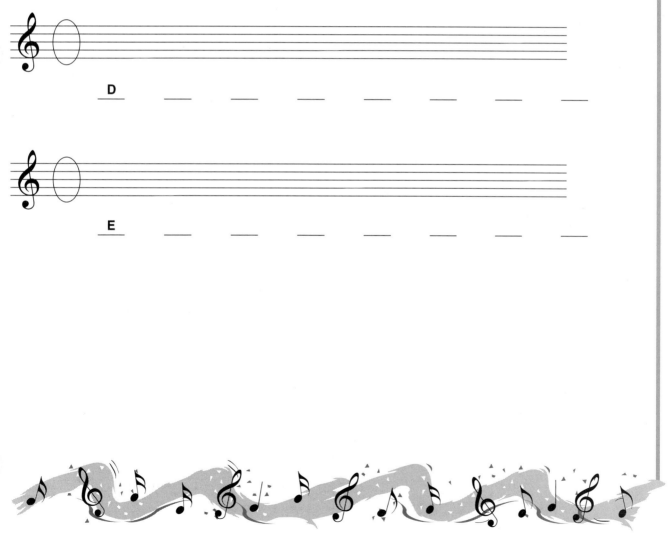

Notate the pitches of the natural minor scale on the staff starting on D, then on E. What notes will you need to fit the pattern of whole and half steps? Mark them in the key signature. Write the letter names of the notes in the spaces below the staff.

MUSIC READING WORKSHEET 16

The Harmonic Minor Scale

Sing this scale from bottom to top and back down again, using pitch syllables and hand signs. What note is missing? Write the missing pitch syllable in the circle.

Draw a circle around the notes that are a half step apart.

Sing the scale again using numbers.

la

◯

fa

mi

re

do

ti,

la,

Now read the harmonic minor scale from the staff. The *do* symbol will help you find your way around. Add the missing pitch syllable in the space below.

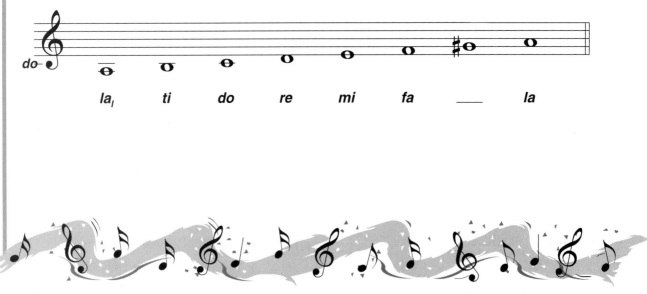

MUSIC READING WORKSHEET 16 (CONTINUED)

Another Minor Scale

Write the scale degree numbers of the harmonic minor scale, from *la₁* to *la* below the scale. Use *si* in place of *so*. Then write the pattern of whole and half steps above it. What do you notice about the distance between *fa* and *si*?

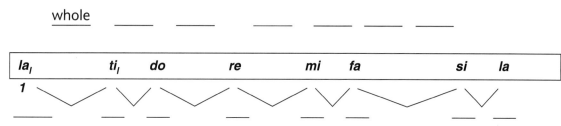

Notate the pitches of the harmonic minor scale on the staff starting on D, then on E. What accidentals will you need to fit the pattern of whole and half steps? Write the letter names of the notes in the spaces below the staff.

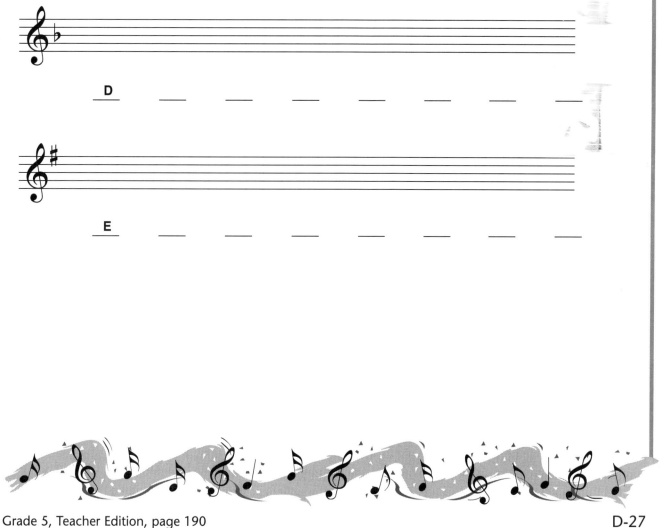

Music Reading Worksheet 17

A New Rhythm

Clap the rhythm as you sing the melody of "Oh, Watch the Stars."

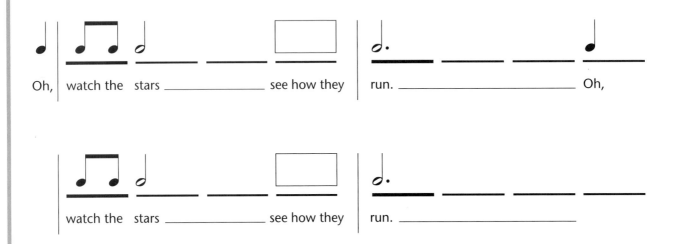

Oh, | watch the stars _____ see how they | run. _____ Oh,

watch the stars _____ see how they | run. _____

How many sounds do you hear on the beats in the boxes? How are those sounds arranged on the beat?

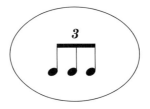

This rhythm symbol is called a *triplet*. It is used to show three even sounds on a beat in simple meter ($\frac{2}{4}$, $\frac{3}{4}$, or $\frac{4}{4}$).

Use the triplet to fill in the missing rhythms.

Grade 5, Teacher Edition, page 216

MUSIC READING WORKSHEET 17 (CONTINUED)

Clap and count the rhythm of this mystery song. Find it in your book.

MUSIC READING WORKSHEET 18

Augmenting and Diminishing Rhythms

Read the rhythm pattern below. Which patterns will sound twice as fast? Twice as slow?

Sing "Old Abram Brown" with each rhythm pattern. How far in the lyrics did you get with each one?

MUSIC READING WORKSHEET 19

A New Scale; a New Mode

Using pitch syllables and hand signs, sing the mixolydian scale, starting on G. Watch out for the half steps. Number the scale degrees in the spaces below the scale.

so,	la,	ti,	do	re	mi	fa	so
1							

Now sing the mixolydian scale starting on *do*. Remember to use the new note, *ta*. Number the scale degrees in the spaces below the scale.

do	re	mi	fa	so	la	ta	do'
1							

Notate the mixolydian scale on the staff starting on G, then on F. What notes will you need to fit the pattern of whole and half steps? Write the letter names of the notes in the spaces below the staff.

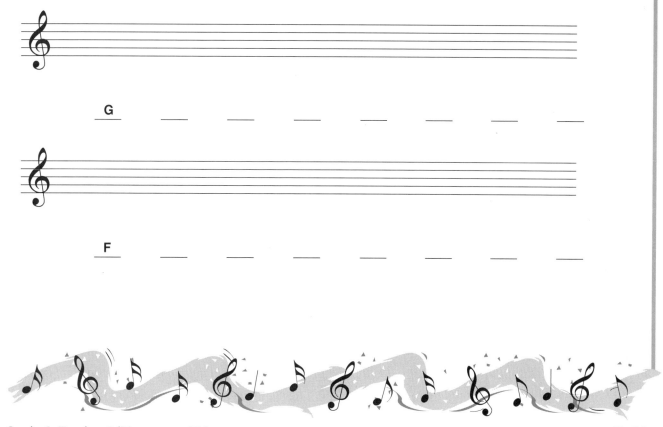

G ___ ___ ___ ___ ___ ___ ___

F ___ ___ ___ ___ ___ ___ ___

MUSIC READING WORKSHEET 20

A Minor Mode

Number the scale degrees of the dorian scale from *re* to *re^l* in the spaces below the staff. Then sing the scale using pitch syllables and hand signs.

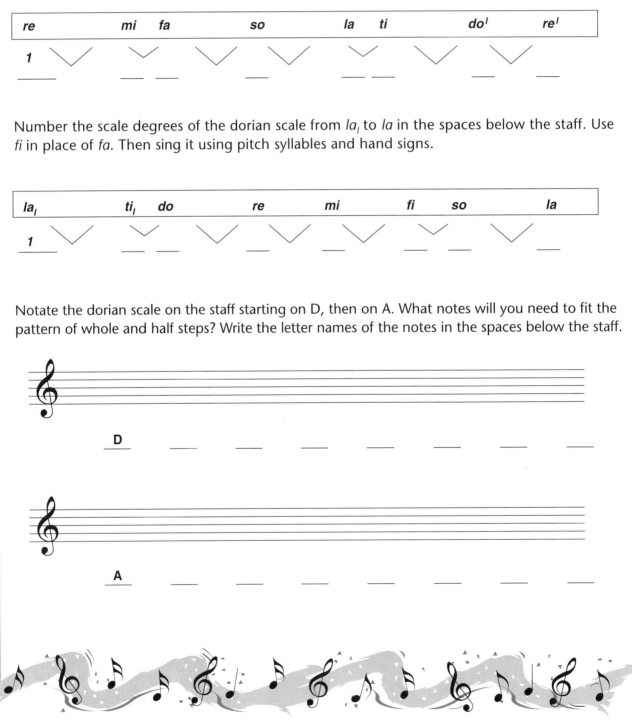

| re | | mi | fa | | so | | la | ti | | do^l | | re^l |
| 1 | | | | | | | | | | | | |

Number the scale degrees of the dorian scale from *la_l* to *la* in the spaces below the staff. Use *fi* in place of *fa*. Then sing it using pitch syllables and hand signs.

| la_l | | ti_l | do | | re | | mi | | fi | so | | la |
| 1 | | | | | | | | | | | | |

Notate the dorian scale on the staff starting on D, then on A. What notes will you need to fit the pattern of whole and half steps? Write the letter names of the notes in the spaces below the staff.

D ___ ___ ___ ___ ___ ___ ___

A ___ ___ ___ ___ ___ ___ ___

Grade 5, Teacher Edition, page 232

MUSIC READING WORKSHEET 21

Curwen Hand Signs

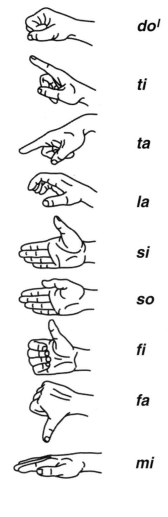

do^l

ti

ta

la

si

so

fi

fa

mi

re

do

Teacher Notes

MUSIC READING PRACTICE
Table of Contents

UNIT 1

Rhythm: Reading Meter in 4—*Laredo* E-2

Rhythm: Reading ♪ ♩ ♪ —*Morning Comes Early* E-3

Melody: Reading Note Names (C-D-E-G-A)—*Bound for South Australia* E-4

Melody: Reading Pentatonic Patterns—*This Train* E-5

UNIT 2

Rhythm: Reading ♫♫ and ♫♫ —*California* E-6

Rhythm: Reading ♫♫ , ♫♫ , and ♫♫♫ —*Drill, Ye Tarriers* E-7

Melody: Reading *fa*—*A la puerta del cielo* (At the Gate of Heaven) E-8

Melody: Reading *do, re, mi, fa, so,* and *la*—*Da pacem, Domine* (Grant Us Peace) E-9

UNIT 3

Rhythm: Reading ♩. and ♪—*Himmel und Erde* (Music Alone Shall Live) E-10

Rhythm: Reading Dotted-Rhythm Patterns—*Don't You Hear the Lambs?* E-11

Melody: Reading *low ti*—*All Through the Night* E-12

Melody: Reading *low ti*—*Dundai* E-13

UNIT 4

Rhythm: Reading ♩. ♪—*Wabash Cannon Ball* E-14

Rhythm: Reading Dotted-Rhythm Patterns—*Scotland the Brave*. E-15

Melody: Reading a Diatonic Major Scale—*Las velitas* (Candles Burning Bright) E-16

Melody: Reading a Melodic Sequence—*Autumn Canon* E-17

UNIT 5

Rhythm: Reading in Compound Meter—*Las estrellitas del cielo* (Stars of the Heavens) . . E-18

Rhythm: Reading in 6/8 Meter—*Blow the Wind Southerly* E-19

Melody: Reading the Natural Minor Scale—*Johnny Has Gone for a Soldier* E-20

Melody: Reading the Harmonic Minor Scale—*Go Down, Moses* E-21

UNIT 6

Rhythm: Reading Triplets—*Oh, Watch the Stars* E-22

Rhythm: Reading Augmentation and Diminution—*Old Abram Brown* E-23

Melody: Reading in Mixolydian Mode—*The Greenland Whale Fishery* E-24

Melody: Reading in Dorian Mode—*Connemara Lullaby* E-25

© PEARSON EDUCATION, INC.

MUSIC READING PRACTICE: SEQUENCE 1

Rhythm: Reading Meter in 4

Use rhythm syllables to **read** and **perform** this counter-rhythm.

Laredo

Folk Song from Mexico

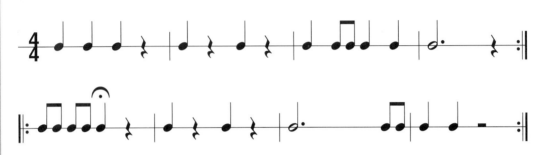

MUSIC READING PRACTICE: SEQUENCE 2

Rhythm: Reading ♪ ♩ ♪

Use rhythm syllables to **read** and **perform** this rhythm accompaniment.

Morning Comes Early

Slovak Folk Song

MUSIC READING PRACTICE: SEQUENCE 3

Melody: Reading Note Names (C-D-E-G-A)

Read and **sing** this countermelody. Use pitch syllables and hand signs.

Bound for South Australia

Sea Shanty

MUSIC READING PRACTICE: SEQUENCE 4

Melody: Reading Pentatonic Patterns

For inner hearing practice, use pitch syllables and hand signs to **read** and **sing** this countermelody.

This Train

African American Spiritual

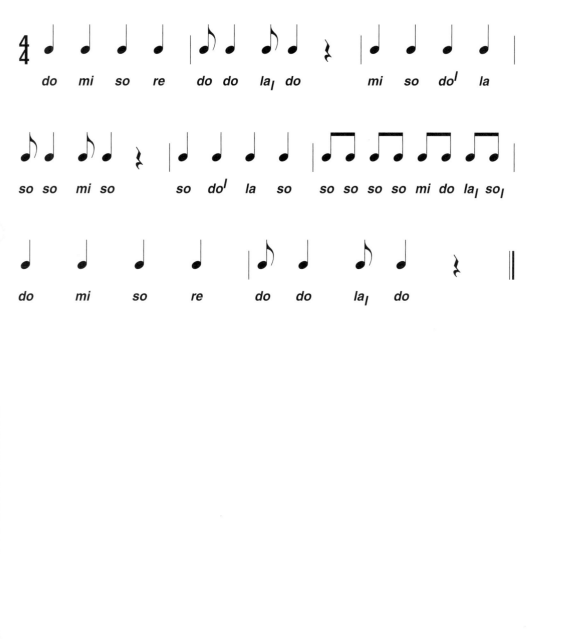

READING PRACTICE

MUSIC READING PRACTICE: SEQUENCE 5

Rhythm: Reading ♫♪ and ♪♫

Use rhythm syllables to **read** and **perform** this two-part rhythm accompaniment.

California

Folk Song from the United States

MUSIC READING PRACTICE: SEQUENCE 6

Rhythm: Reading ♪♫, ♫♪, and ♪♫♫

Use rhythm syllables to **read** and **perform** this counter-rhythm.

Drill, Ye Tarriers

Words and Music by Thomas Casey

MUSIC READING PRACTICE: SEQUENCE 7

Melody: Reading *fa*

Read and **sing** this two-part countermelody. Use pitch syllables and hand signs.

A la puerta del cielo (At the Gate of Heaven)   *Folk Song from Spain*

MUSIC READING PRACTICE: SEQUENCE 8

Melody: Reading *do, re, mi, fa, so,* and *la*

Read and **sing** this countermelody. Use pitch syllables and hand signs.

Da pacem, Domine (Grant Us Peace)

Music by Melchior Franck

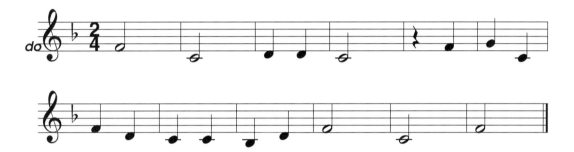

READING PRACTICE

MUSIC READING PRACTICE: SEQUENCE 9

Rhythm: Reading 𝅘𝅥𝅭 and 𝅘𝅥𝅮

Use rhythm syllables to **read** and **perform** this counter-rhythm.

Himmel und Erde (Music Alone Shall Live)

Round from Germany

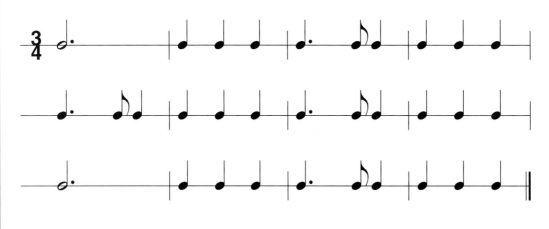

Grade 5, Teacher Edition, page 94

MUSIC READING PRACTICE: SEQUENCE 10

Rhythm: Reading Dotted-Rhythm Patterns

Use rhythm syllables to **read** and **perform** this counter-rhythm.

Don't You Hear the Lambs?

Folk Hymn from the Southern United States

READING PRACTICE

MUSIC READING PRACTICE: SEQUENCE 11

Melody: Reading *low ti*

Read and **sing** this two-part countermelody. Use pitch syllables and hand signs.

All Through the Night

Melody from Wales

Grade 5, Teacher Edition, page 105

MUSIC READING PRACTICE: SEQUENCE 12

Melody: Reading *low ti*

Read and **sing** this two-part countermelody. Use pitch syllables and hand signs.

Dundai

Folk Song from Israel

MUSIC READING PRACTICE: SEQUENCE 13

Rhythm: Reading

Use rhythm syllables to **read** and **perform** this counter-rhythm.

Wabash Cannon Ball

Traditional

Grade 5, Teacher Edition, page 136

MUSIC READING PRACTICE: SEQUENCE 14

Rhythm: Reading Dotted-Rhythm Patterns

Use rhythm syllables to **read** and **perform** this counter-rhythm.

Scotland the Brave

Traditional Melody from Scotland

© PEARSON EDUCATION, INC.

MUSIC READING PRACTICE: SEQUENCE 15

Melody: Reading a Diatonic Major Scale

Read and **sing** this countermelody. Use pitch syllables and hand signs.

Las velitas (Candles Burning Bright)

Folk Song from Mexico

Grade 5, Teacher Edition, page 147

MUSIC READING PRACTICE: SEQUENCE 16

Melody: Reading a Melodic Sequence

Read and **sing** this countermelody. Use pitch syllables and hand signs.

Autumn Canon

Words by Sean Diebler
Music by Lajos Bárdos

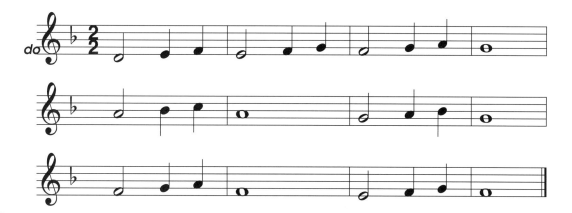

READING PRACTICE

Music Reading Practice: Sequence 17

Rhythm: Reading in Compound Meter

Use rhythm syllables to **read** and **perform** this two-part rhythm accompaniment.

Las estrellitas del cielo (Stars of the Heavens)   *Folk Song from Spain*

MUSIC READING PRACTICE: SEQUENCE 18

Rhythm: Reading in $\frac{6}{8}$ Meter

Use rhythm syllables to **read** and **perform** this rhythm accompaniment.

Blow the Wind Southerly

Folk Song from Northumbria

READING PRACTICE

MUSIC READING PRACTICE: SEQUENCE 19

Melody: Reading the Natural Minor Scale

Read and **sing** this countermelody. Use pitch syllables and hand signs.

Johnny Has Gone for a Soldier

Song of the American Revolution
Collected by John Allison

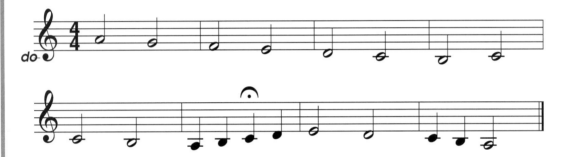

E-20

© PEARSON EDUCATION, INC.

MUSIC READING PRACTICE: SEQUENCE 20

Melody: Reading the Harmonic Minor Scale

Read and **sing** this two-part countermelody. Use pitch syllables and hand signs.

Go Down, Moses

African American Spiritual

© PEARSON EDUCATION, INC.

READING PRACTICE

MUSIC READING PRACTICE: SEQUENCE 21

Rhythm: Reading Triplets

Use rhythm syllables to **read** and **perform** this counter-rhythm.

Oh, Watch the Stars

Folk Song from South Carolina

MUSIC READING PRACTICE: SEQUENCE 22

Rhythm: Reading Augmentation and Diminution

Use rhythm syllables to **read** and **perform** this three-part rhythm accompaniment.

Old Abram Brown

Words by Walter de la Mare
Music by Benjamin Britten

READING PRACTICE

MUSIC READING PRACTICE: SEQUENCE 23

Melody: Reading in Mixolydian Mode

Read and **sing** this countermelody. Use pitch syllables and hand signs.

The Greenland Whale Fishery

*Newfoundland Version of a
British Sea Song*

Grade 5, Teacher Edition, page 230

MUSIC READING PRACTICE: SEQUENCE 24

Melody: Reading in Dorian Mode

Read and **sing** this countermelody. Use pitch syllables and hand signs.

Connemara Lullaby

Words by Julie Scott
Folk Melody from Ireland

READING PRACTICE

Teacher Notes

ORFF

Table of Contents

Morning Comes Early. F-2

Arirang F-4

I Love the Mountains F-5

Drill, Ye Tarriers F-6

De colores F-9

Joshua Fought the Battle of Jericho F-12

Dundai F-14

Roll On, Columbia F-15

This Land is Your Land F-17

Wabash Cannon Ball F-18

Autumn Canon F-19

Las estrellitas del cielo (Stars of the Heavens) F-20

Don Alfonso F-21

Blow the Wind Southerly F-22

Pat Works on the Railway F-24

Mango Walk F-26

Old Abram Brown F-27

Down by the Riverside F-28

Shenandoah F-30

Camptown Races F-31

Woke Up This Morning F-33

Ah ya Zane (Zane from Abedeen) F-37

Se va el caimán (The Alligator) F-39

La Jesusita F-41

St. Louis Blues F-43

Zum gali gali F-45

Instrumentarium **F-46**

ORFF

ORFF 1

Morning Comes Early

Slovak Folk Song
Arranged by Konnie Saliba

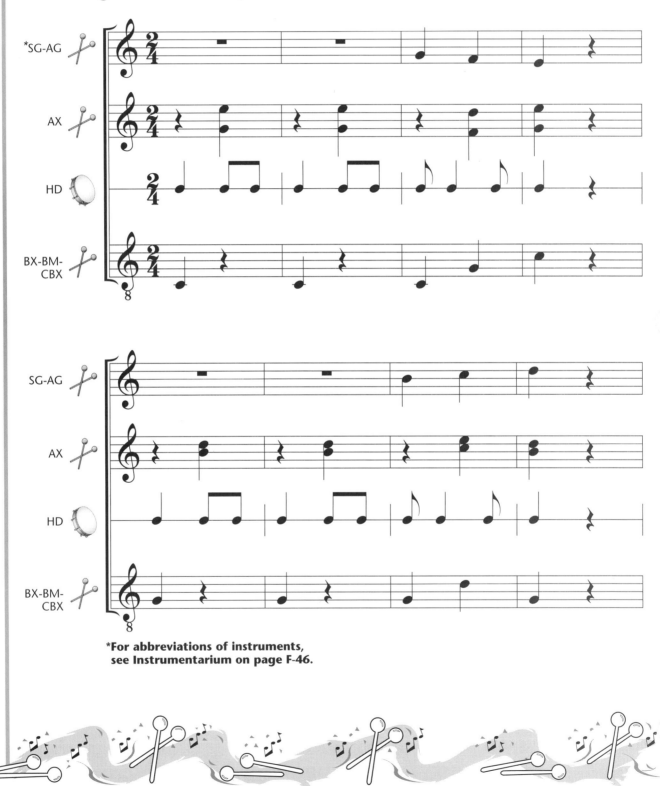

*For abbreviations of instruments,
see Instrumentarium on page F-46.

ORFF 1 (CONTINUED)

ORFF

ORFF 2

Arirang

Folk Song from Korea
Arranged by Konnie Saliba

(use wooden mallets on Bass Metallophone)

Grade 5, Teacher Edition, page 24

ORFF 3

I Love the Mountains

Traditional
Arranged by Danai Gagne

ORFF 4

Drill, Ye Tarriers

Words and Music by Thomas Casey
Arranged by Paul Kerlee

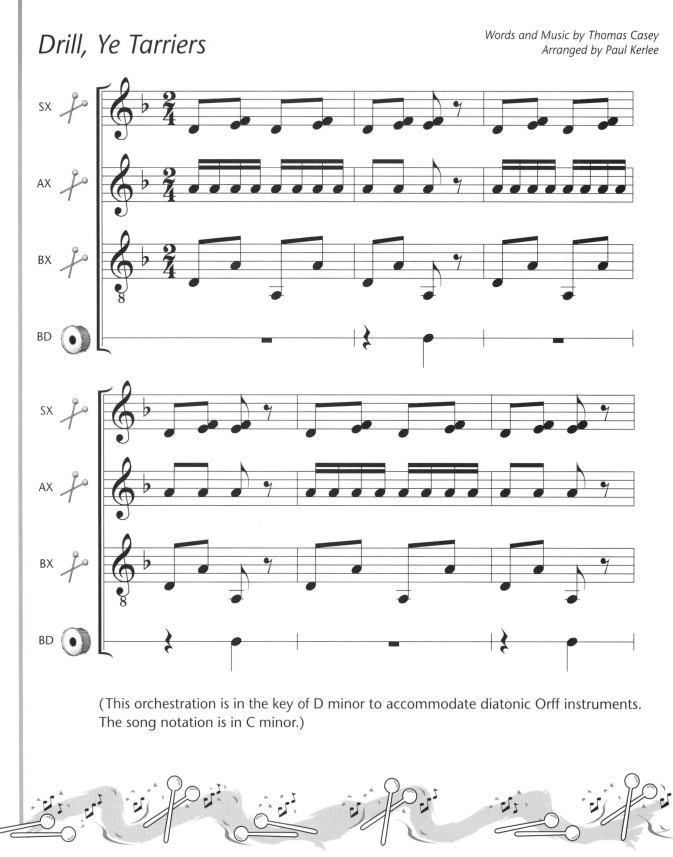

(This orchestration is in the key of D minor to accommodate diatonic Orff instruments. The song notation is in C minor.)

Orff 4 (continued)

ORFF

Orff 4 (continued)

ORFF 5

De colores

Folk Song from Mexico

ORFF

ORFF 5 (CONTINUED)

ORFF 5 (CONTINUED)

ORFF

ORFF 6

Joshua Fought the Battle of Jericho

African American Spiritual
Arranged by Konnie Saliba

CBX - stems down

Grade 5, Teacher Edition, page 100

ORFF 6 (CONTINUED)

ORFF

Orff 7

Dundai

Folk Song from Israel
Arranged by Konnie Saliba

CBX - stems down

Grade 5, Teacher Edition, page 106

ORFF 8

Roll On, Columbia

Music Based on "Goodnight, Irene" by
Huddie Ledbetter and John A. Lomax
Arranged by Konnie Saliba

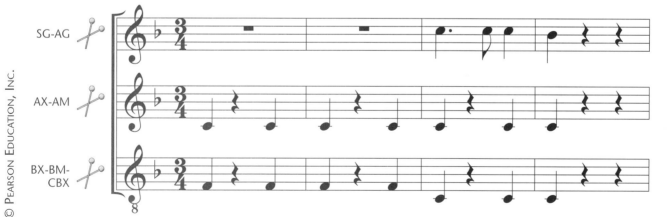

© PEARSON EDUCATION, INC.

ORFF

ORFF 8 (CONTINUED)

Grade 5, Teacher Edition, page 116

ORFF 9

This Land Is Your Land

Words and Music by Woody Guthrie
Arranged by Konnie Saliba

TRO © Copyright 1956 (Renewed) 1958 (Renewed) Ludlow Music Publishers, Inc., New York, NY. Used by Permission.

CBX part may be doubled on guitar.

ORFF

ORFF 10

Wabash Cannon Ball

Traditional
Arranged by Konnie Saliba

(add SG-AG and Tam on Refrain)

CBX part may be doubled on guitar.

Orff 11

Autumn Canon

Music by Lajos Bárdos
Arranged by Konnie Saliba

SG-AG

AX-AM

FC

BX-BM-CBX

SG-AG

AX-AM

FC

BX-BM-CBX

Orchestration is intended for unison singing or playing melody.

Suggest: Sing with accompaniment or melody played with accompaniment.

Play in 4-part canon twice in this order:

    1) alto xylophone and metallophone

    2) basses

    3) glockenspiels

    4) soprano xylophone and metallophone

Sing with accompaniment.

ORFF

ORFF 12

Las estrellitas del cielo (Stars of Heavens)

Folk Song from Spain
Arranged by Konnie Saliba

ORFF 13

Don Alfonso

Folk Song from Spain
Arranged by Konnie Saliba

ORFF

ORFF 14

Blow the Wind Southerly

Folk Song from Northumbria
Arranged by Danai Gagne

Grade 5, Teacher Edition, page 178

ORFF 14 (CONTINUED)

ORFF

ORFF 15

Pat Works on the Railway

Irish American Railroad Song
Arranged by Konnie Saliba

Grade 5, Teacher Edition, page 182

ORFF 15 (CONTINUED)

*add CBX on B section

ORFF

ORFF 16

Mango Walk

Calypso Song from Jamaica
Arranged by Konnie Saliba

(3 times)

ORFF 17

Old Abram Brown

Music by Benjamin Britten
Arranged by Judith Thomas

(Play AG part and upper AX part only when song is sung in unison.)

ORFF 18

Down by the Riverside

African American Spiritual
Arranged by Konnie Saliba

ORFF 18 (CONTINUED)

ORFF 19

Shenandoah

Capstan Sea Shanty
Arranged by Konnie Saliba

Orff 20

Camptown Races

Words and Music by Stephen Foster
Arranged by Konnie Saliba

Orff

ORFF 20 (CONTINUED)

Grade 5, Teacher Edition, page 270

ORFF 21 (CONTINUED)

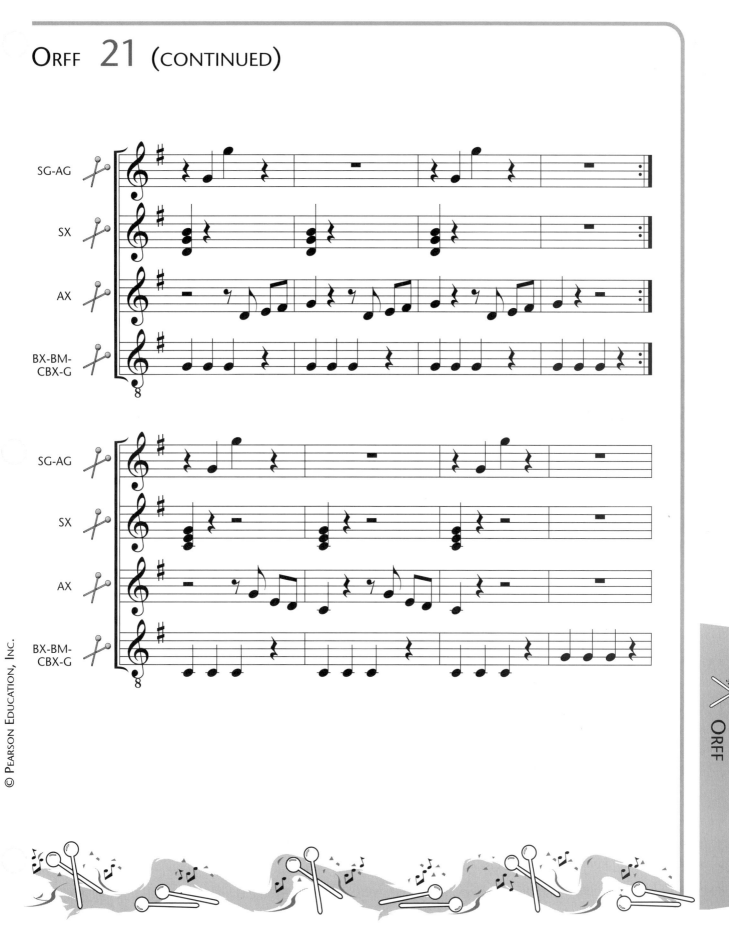

SG-AG

SX

AX

BX-BM-
CBX-G

ORFF

ORFF 21 (CONTINUED)

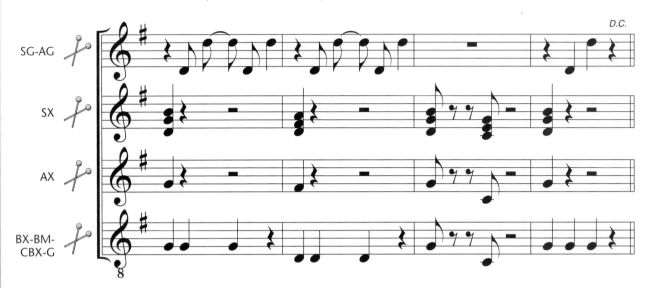

SG-AG
SX
AX
BX-BM-CBX-G

Grade 5, Teacher Edition, page 288

ORFF 22

Ah ya Zane (Zane from Abedeen)

Arabic Folk Song
Arranged by Konnie Saliba

ORFF

ORFF 22 (CONTINUED)

ORFF 23

Se va el caimán (The Alligator)

Dance Song from Colombia
Arranged by Konnie Saliba

ORFF

ORFF 23 (CONTINUED)

Ostinato (can be played throughout)

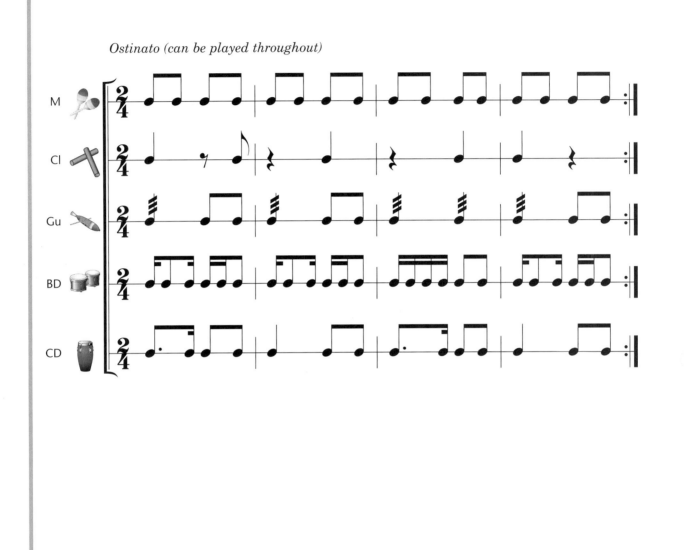

© PEARSON EDUCATION, INC.

ORFF 24

La Jesusita

Folk Song from Mexico
Arranged by Konnie Saliba

ORFF

ORFF 24 (CONTINUED)

Grade 5, Teacher Edition, page 322

ORFF 25

St. Louis Blues

Words and Music by W. C. Handy
Arranged by Konnie Saliba

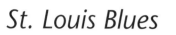

ORFF

ORFF 25 (CONTINUED)

(This orchestration is in the key of G major to accommodate diatonic Orff instruments. The song notation is in F major.)

Orff 26

Zum gali gali

Folk Song from Israel
Arranged by Konnie Saliba

ORFF 27

INSTRUMENTARIUM

Abbreviations of Instruments on a Score

Winds

SoR	Sopranino Recorder
SR	Soprano Recorder
AR	Alto Recorder
TR	Tenor Recorder
BR	Bass Recorder

Mallet Instruments

SG	Soprano Glockenspiel
AG	Alto Glockenspiel
SX	Soprano Xylophone
AX	Alto Xylophone
BX	Bass Xylophone
CBX	Contrabass Xylophone
SM	Soprano Metallophone
AM	Alto Metallophone
BM	Bass Metallophone
CBB	Contrabass Bars

Percussion—Metals

Tr	Triangle
FC	Finger Cymbals
JB	Jingle Bells
BT	Bell Tree
AB	Agogo Bells
CB	Cow Bell
Cym	Cymbals
W	Slide Whistle

Percussion—Woods

WB	Wood Block
ToB	Tone Block

C	Castanets
Sh	Shakers
M	Maracas
Cb	Cabasa
R	Ratchet
Rt	Rattles
TeB	Temple Blocks
VS	Vibra Slap
Cl	Claves
Gu	Guiro
LD	Log Drum
SB	Sand Blocks
Af	Afuchi

Percussion—Membranes or Skins

HD	Hand Drum
Tam	Tambourine
BD	Bongo Drums
CD	Conga Drum
SD	Snare Drum

Large Percussion

HC	Hanging Cymbal
G	Gong
BD	Bass Drum

Tuned Instruments

G	Guitar
P	Piano
Tp	Timpani
DB	Double Bass

SIGNING

Table of Contents

This Train G-2

Stand By Me G-3

All Through the Night G-5

Kum Ba Yah G-7

You've Got a Friend G-10

Río, río (River, River) G-12

Freedom Is Coming G-13

America G-14

Manual Alphabet **G-16**

Numbers **G-17**

SIGNING 1

This Train

African American Spiritual

train	go	heaven
This train is	bound for	glory, this train.

train	go	heaven
This train is	bound for	glory,

carry	people	good	holy
don't carry	none but the	good and	holy.

train	go	heaven
This train is	bound for	glory, this train.

① sign directed up toward heaven

In this song, "bound" and "carry" are both directional signs. The sign for "bound" should move toward heaven, because the train is "bound for glory" or heaven. The sign for "carry" should also move toward heaven because the train is carrying "none but the good and holy" to heaven.

Grade 5, Teacher Edition, page 26

SIGNING 2

Stand By Me

*Words and Music by Ben E. King,
Jerry Lieber, and Mike Stoller*

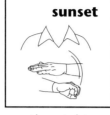

when

When

sunset

the night

night

has come,

dark

And the land is dark,

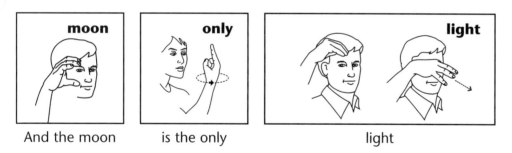

moon

And the moon

only

is the only

light

light

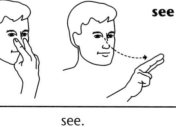

we

we'll

see

see.

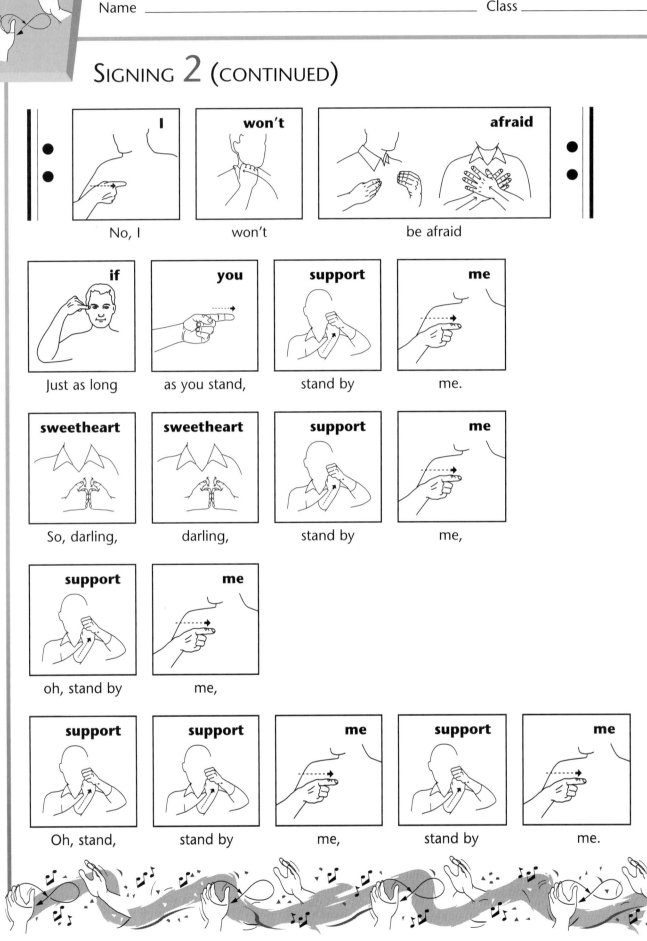

SIGNING 2 (CONTINUED)

I **won't** **afraid**

No, I   won't   be afraid

if **you** **support** **me**

Just as long   as you stand,   stand by   me.

sweetheart **sweetheart** **support** **me**

So, darling,   darling,   stand by   me,

support **me**

oh, stand by   me,

support **support** **me** **support** **me**

Oh, stand,   stand by   me,   stand by   me.

SIGNING 3

All Through the Night

*Melody from Wales
Verse by Harold Boulton*

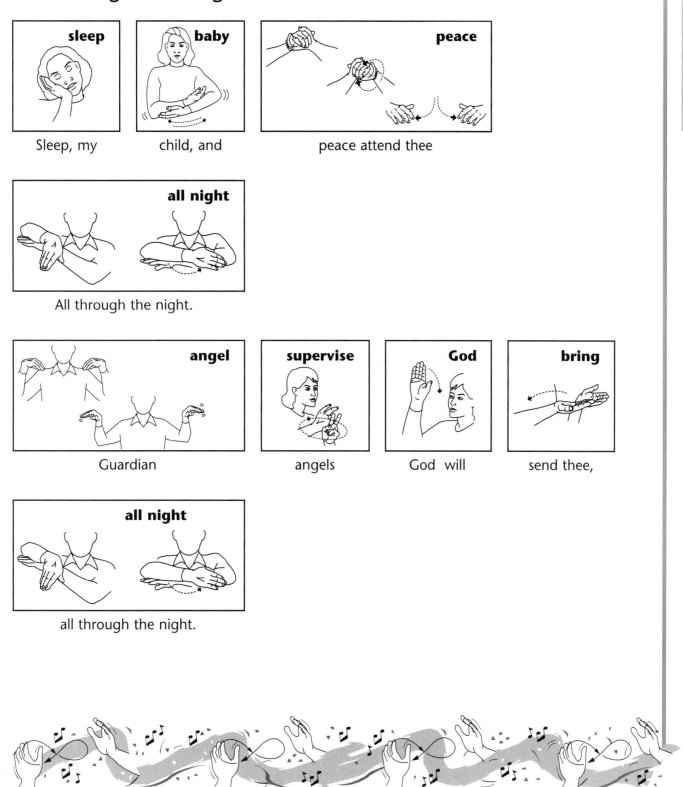

sleep

Sleep, my

baby

child, and

peace

peace attend thee

all night

All through the night.

angel

Guardian

supervise

angels

God

God will

bring

send thee,

all night

all through the night.

Signing 3 (continued)

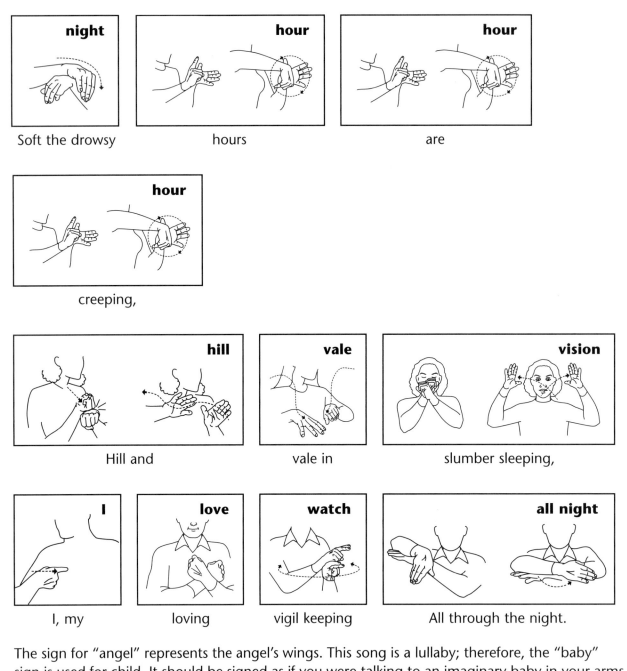

night	**hour**	**hour**
Soft the drowsy	hours	are

hour

creeping,

hill	**vale**	**vision**
Hill and	vale in	slumber sleeping,

I	**love**	**watch**	**all night**
I, my	loving	vigil keeping	All through the night.

The sign for "angel" represents the angel's wings. This song is a lullaby; therefore, the "baby" sign is used for child. It should be signed as if you were talking to an imaginary baby in your arms. "Send" is a directional sign; therefore, the sign should move from heaven to the child.

SIGNING 4

Kum Ba Yah

Traditional Song from South Africa

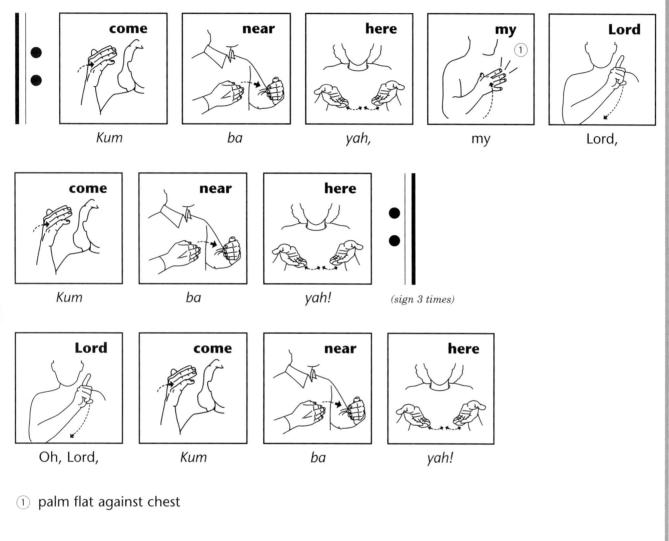

come	near	here	my	Lord
Kum	*ba*	*yah,*	*my*	*Lord,*

come	near	here
Kum	*ba*	*yah!*

(sign 3 times)

Lord	come	near	here
Oh, Lord,	*Kum*	*ba*	*yah!*

① palm flat against chest

SIGNING 4 (CONTINUED)

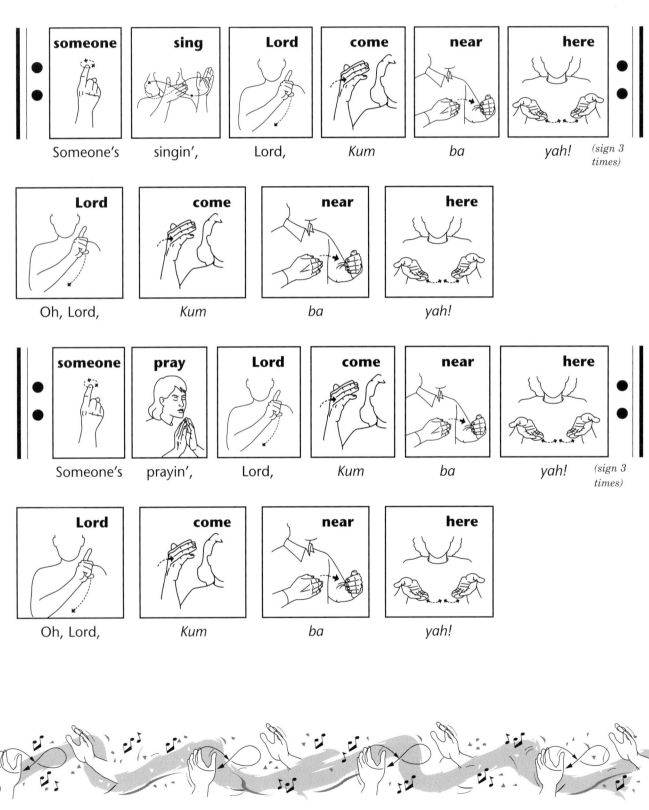

someone	sing	Lord	come	near	here
Someone's	singin',	Lord,	Kum	ba	yah! *(sign 3 times)*

Lord	come	near	here
Oh, Lord,	Kum	ba	yah!

someone	pray	Lord	come	near	here
Someone's	prayin',	Lord,	Kum	ba	yah! *(sign 3 times)*

Lord	come	near	here
Oh, Lord,	Kum	ba	yah!

SIGNING 4 (CONTINUED)

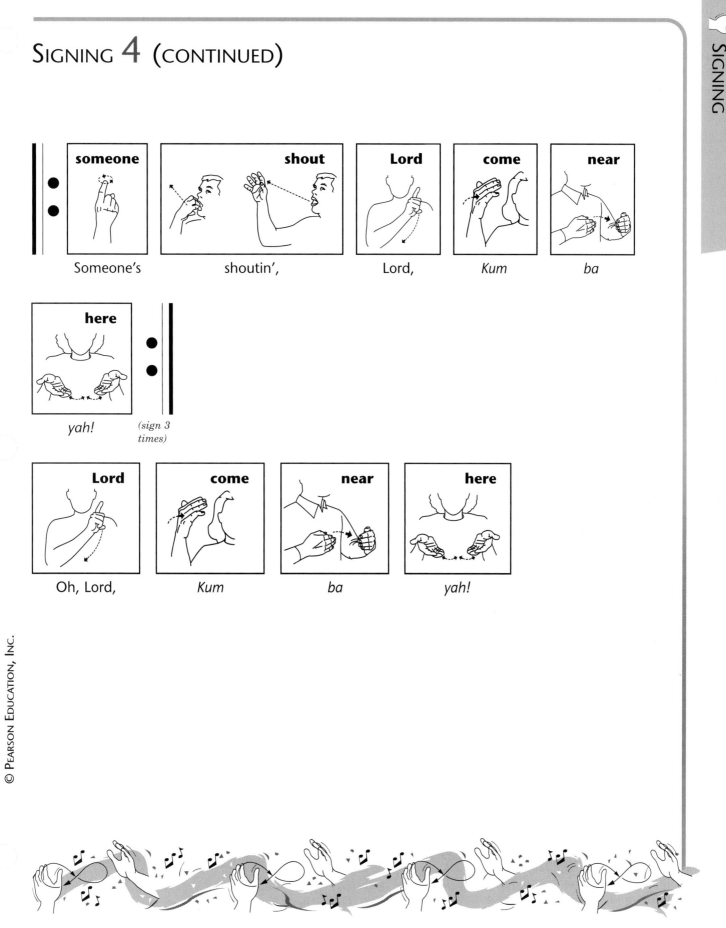

| | someone | shout | Lord | come | near |
| | Someone's | shoutin', | Lord, | *Kum* | *ba* |

| here | (sign 3 times) |
| *yah!* | |

| Lord | come | near | here |
| Oh, Lord, | *Kum* | *ba* | *yah!* |

SIGNING 5

You've Got a Friend

Words and Music by Carole King

REFRAIN

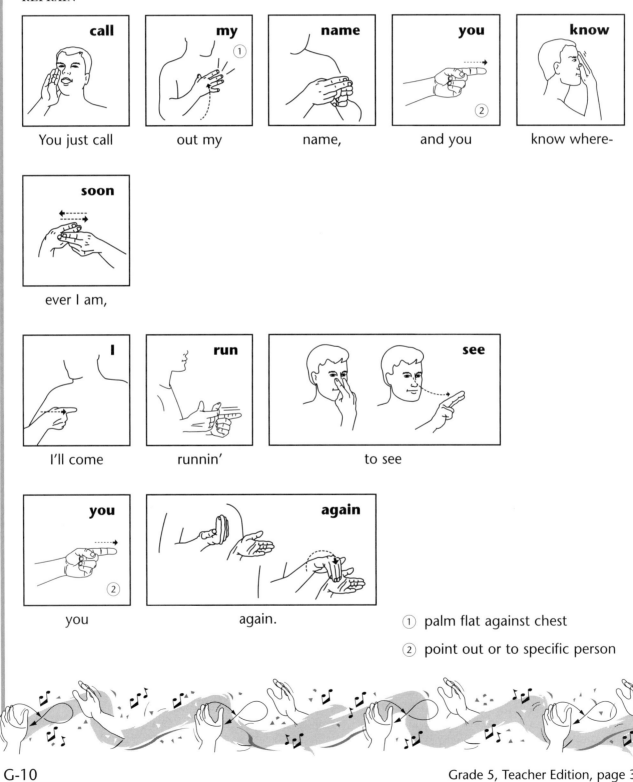

You just call   out my   name,   and you   know where-

ever I am,

I'll come   runnin'   to see

you   again.

① palm flat against chest

② point out or to specific person

SIGNING 5 (CONTINUED)

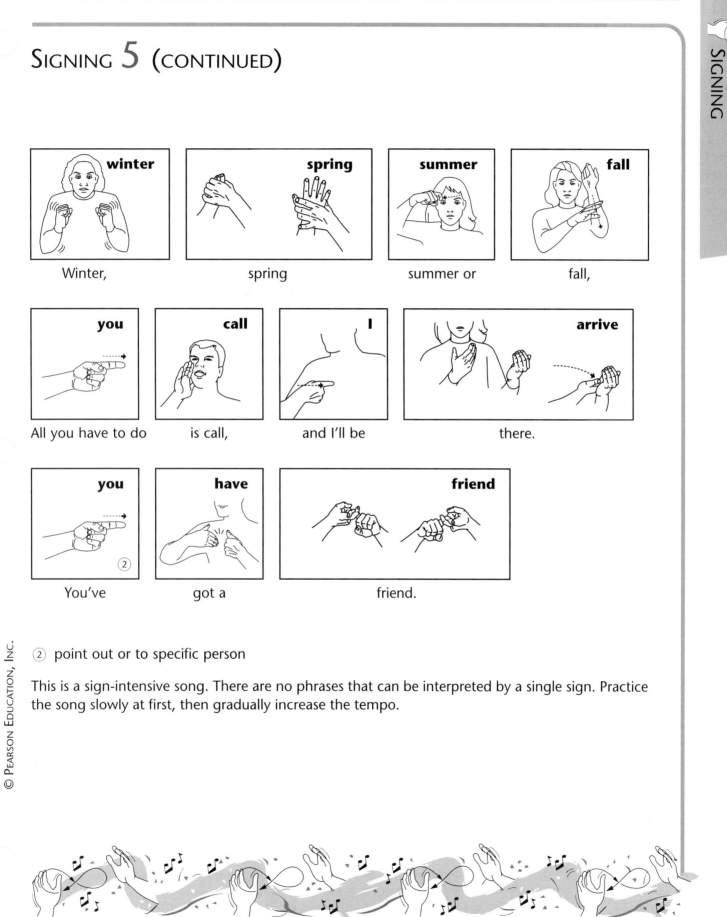

winter	**spring**	**summer**	**fall**
Winter,	spring	summer or	fall,

you	**call**	**I**	**arrive**
All you have to do	is call,	and I'll be	there.

you ②	**have**	**friend**
You've	got a	friend.

② point out or to specific person

This is a sign-intensive song. There are no phrases that can be interpreted by a single sign. Practice the song slowly at first, then gradually increase the tempo.

SIGNING 6

Río, río (River, River)

Traditional Song from Chile
English Words by Alice Firgau

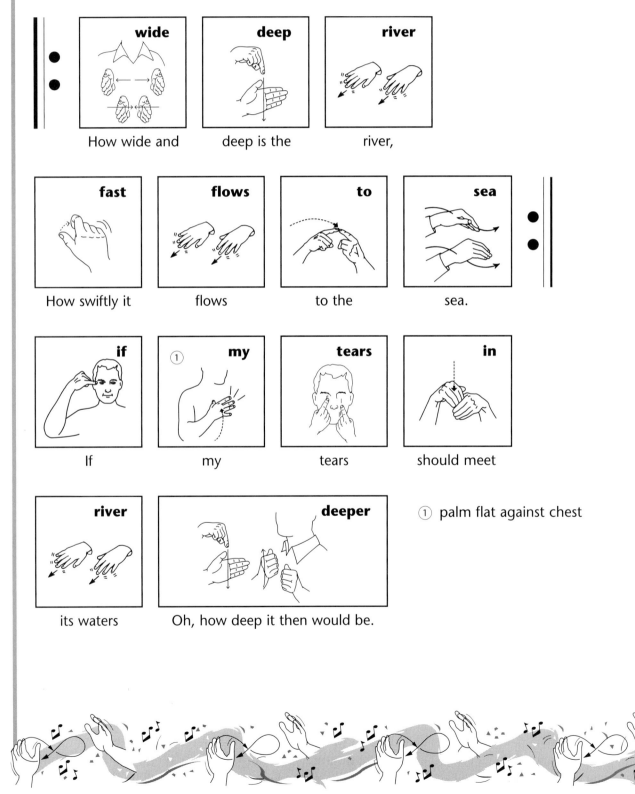

wide — How wide and

deep — deep is the

river — river,

fast — How swiftly it

flows — flows

to — to the

sea — sea.

if — If

① **my** — my

tears — tears

in — should meet

river — its waters

deeper — Oh, how deep it then would be.

① palm flat against chest

Grade 5, Teacher Edition, page 370

SIGNING 7

Freedom Is Coming

Freedom Song from South Africa
Collected by Anders Nyberg

freedom

Oh, freedom,

yes
(gesture:
nod head)

oh yes,

I

I

know

know.

freedom

Freedom

future

is coming.

① **my**

my

spirit

spirit

knows

knows.

① palm flat against chest

Signing 8

America

Words by Samuel Francis Smith
Traditional Melody

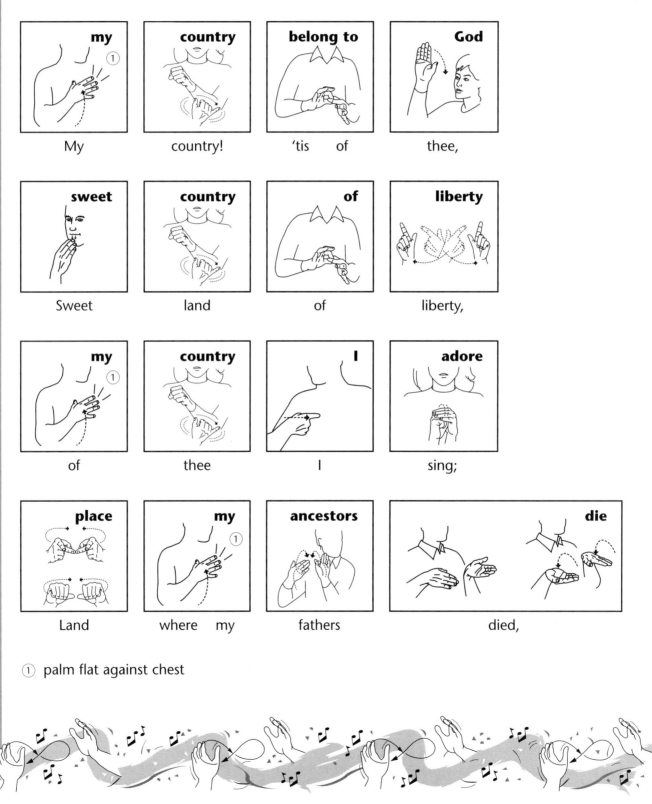

my ① — My

country — country!

belong to — 'tis   of

God — thee,

sweet — Sweet

country — land

of — of

liberty — liberty,

my ① — of

country — thee

I — I

adore — sing;

place — Land

my ① — where   my

ancestors — fathers

die — died,

① palm flat against chest

SIGNING 8 (CONTINUED)

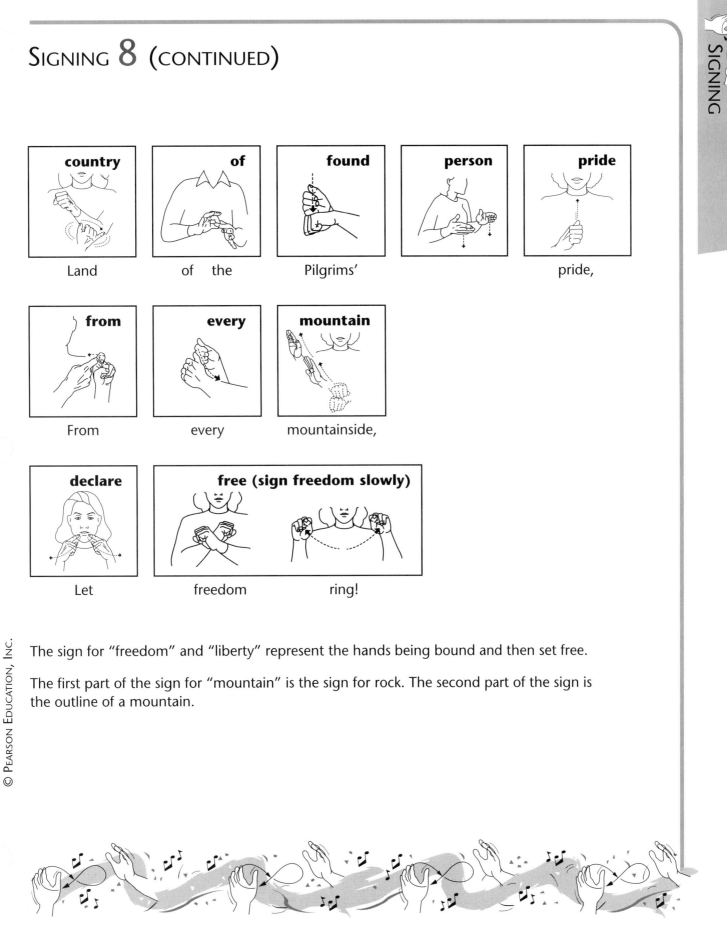

country	**of**	**found**	**person**	**pride**
Land	of the	Pilgrims'		pride,

from	**every**	**mountain**
From	every	mountainside,

declare	**free (sign freedom slowly)**
Let	freedom ring!

The sign for "freedom" and "liberty" represent the hands being bound and then set free.

The first part of the sign for "mountain" is the sign for rock. The second part of the sign is the outline of a mountain.

SIGNING 9

Manual Alphabet

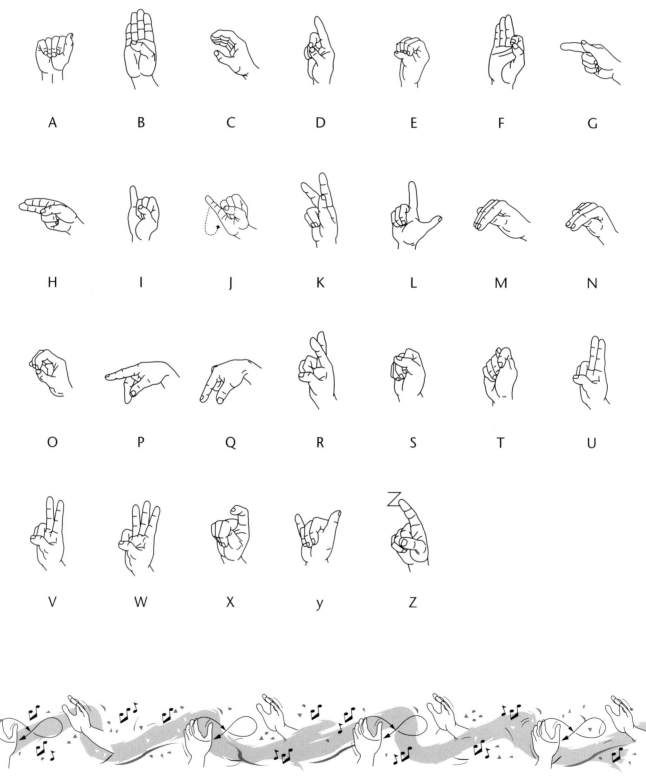

A   B   C   D   E   F   G

H   I   J   K   L   M   N

O   P   Q   R   S   T   U

V   W   X   y   Z

SIGNING 10

Numbers

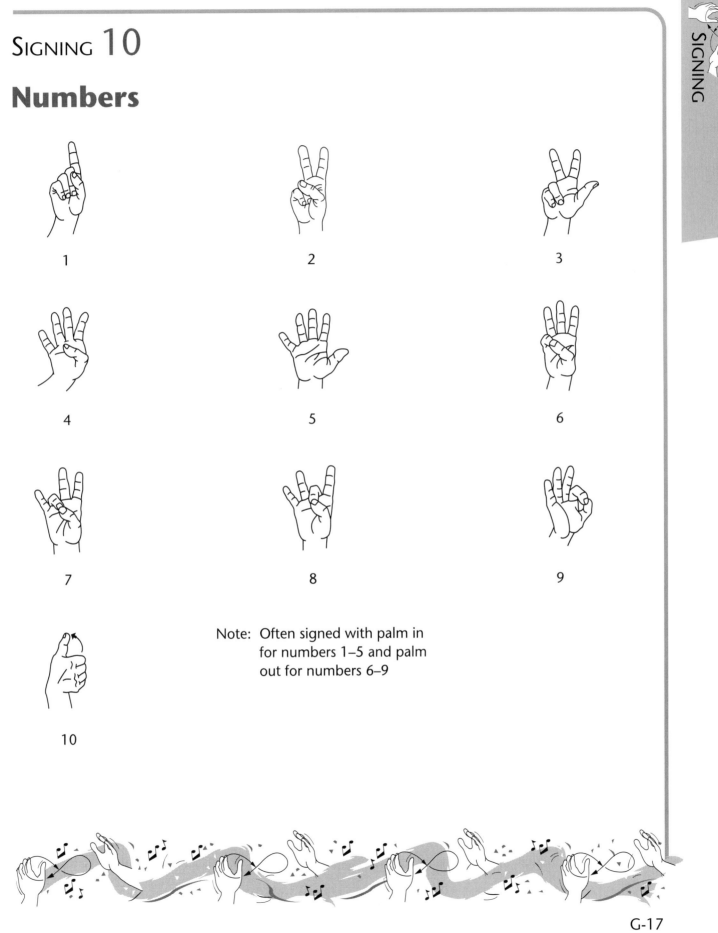

1

2

3

4

5

6

7

8

9

10

Note: Often signed with palm in for numbers 1–5 and palm out for numbers 6–9

Teacher Notes

KEYBOARD

Table of Contents

One-line, Two-line, Three-line Reading H-2

Fingering Steps and Skips Using a One-, Two-, and Three-line Staff H-4

Syncopated Accompaniment—*Éliza Kongo* H-5

Two-Handed Broken-Chord Accompaniment—*Morning Has Broken* H-6

Rhythmic Accompaniment—*Adelita* H-7

Strumming Accompaniment—*Home on the Range* H-9

Playing an Accompaniment in ¾—*De colores* H-11

Playing a Two-Handed Accompaniment—*Scotland the Brave* H-12

Playing a Three-Part Round—*Tumba* H-13

Playing a Two-Handed Broken-Chord Accompaniment—*Blow the Wind
    Southerly* H-14

Playing a Left-Hand Accompaniment—*Johnny Has Gone for a Soldier* H-16

Playing an Accompaniment Using Triplets—*Oh, Watch the Stars* H-17

Playing a Blues Improvisation—*Good Mornin', Blues* H-19

Left-Handed Accompaniment in Steady Beat—*Down By the Riverside* H-20

Two-Handed Syncopation—*Camptown Races* H-21

Rhythmic Accompaniment—*¡Qué bonita bandera!* (What a Beautiful Banner!) . . . H-22

Broken-Chord Accompaniment—*La Jesusita* H-23

Another Left-Hand Accompaniment—*Cattle Call* H-24

Playing a Tritone Accompaniment—*St. Louis Blues* H-25

Playing a "Strumming" Accompaniment—*Blowin' in the Wind* H-26

Playing a Melody in Free Meter—*Ríu ríu chíu* H-27

"Comping" Beneath Scat Syllables—*Now's the Time* H-28

Playing an Introduction and an Interlude—*The Addams Family* H-29

Playing an Ostinato Accompaniment—*Oy, Hanuka* (O, Chanukah) H-30

KEYBOARD

KEYBOARD 1

One-line, Two-line, Three-line Reading

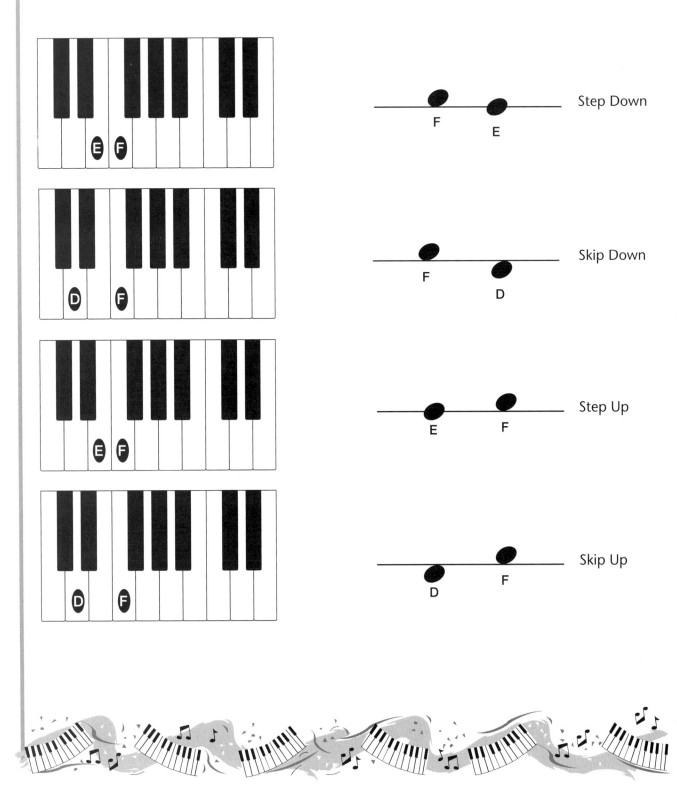

Step Down

Skip Down

Step Up

Skip Up

KEYBOARD 1 (CONTINUED)

One-line, Two-line, Three-line Reading

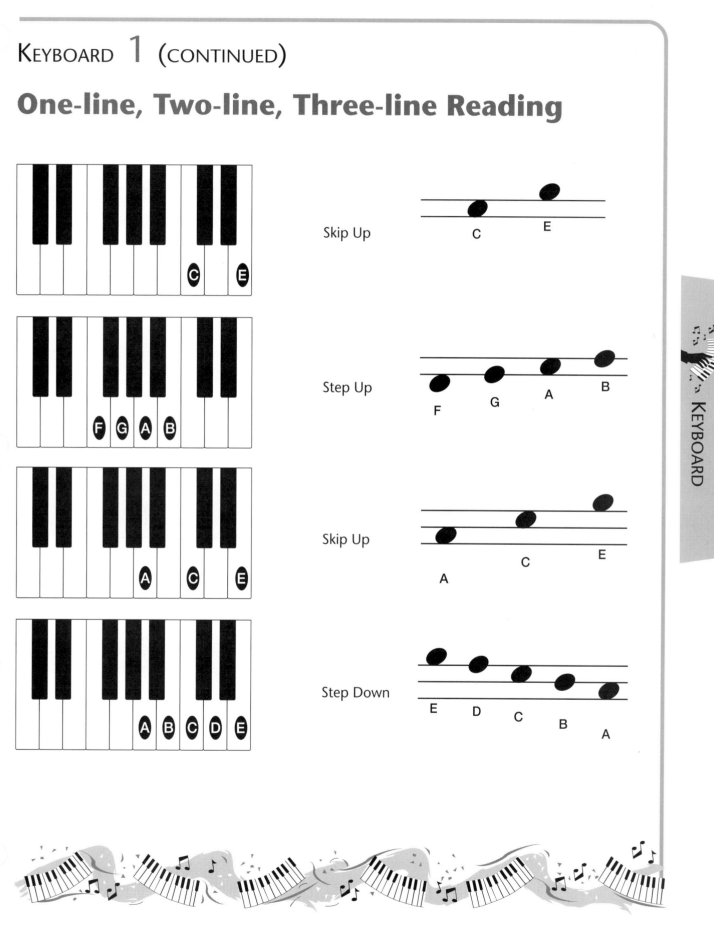

Skip Up   C   E

Step Up   F   G   A   B

Skip Up   A   C   E

Step Down   E   D   C   B   A

KEYBOARD

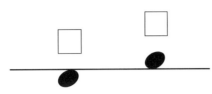

KEYBOARD 2

Fingering Steps and Skips Using a One-, Two-, and Three-line Staff

Which fingers will you use?

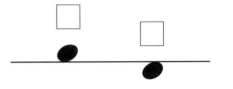

Write your choices in the boxes above the notes.

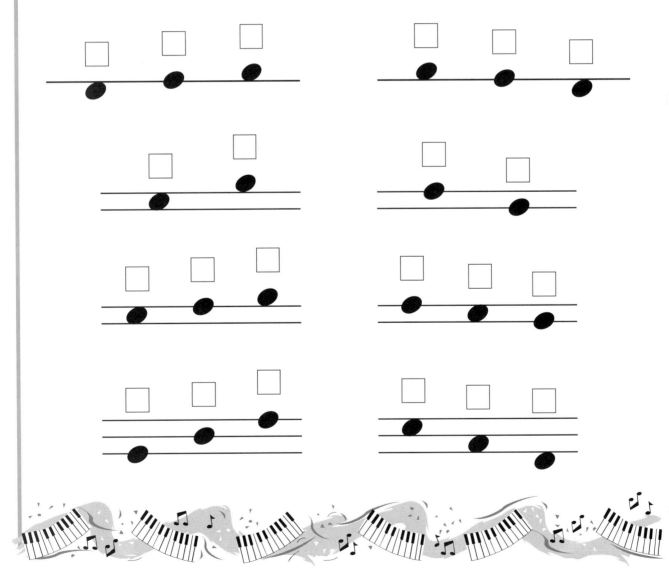

KEYBOARD 3

Syncopated Accompaniment

Éliza Kongo

Traditional Song from Dominica

KEYBOARD 4

Two-Handed Broken-Chord Accompaniment

Morning Has Broken

Traditional Gaelic Melody

KEYBOARD 5

Rhythmic Accompaniment

Adelita

Folk Song from Mexico

Part 1

KEYBOARD 5 (CONTINUED)

Part 2

KEYBOARD 6

Strumming Accompaniment

Home on the Range

Traditional Song from the United States

KEYBOARD 6 (CONTINUED)

Grade 5, Teacher Edition, page 68

KEYBOARD *7*

Playing an Accompaniment in $\frac{3}{4}$

De colores

Folk Song from Mexico

POSSIBLE INTRODUCTION

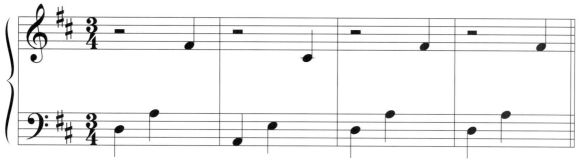

KEYBOARD 8

Playing a Two-Handed Accompaniment

This two-handed accompaniment uses a "crush note" in the right hand. Play this figure with right-hand fingers 2 and 3 in each of the three positions. Both pitches are played simultaneously, then the first pitch or smaller "crush note" is released immediately. Left-hand pitches should be played with the fingering that is comfortable for you.

Scotland the Brave

Traditional Melody from Scotland

Practice each of the three figures until they are comfortable.

  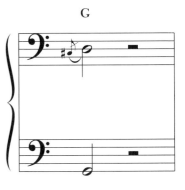

Next, practice this sequence of figures.

C | C | F C | G |

If two figures must be played within one measure, eliminate the rest on beats 3 and 4.

Now practice this sequence.

C | C | F C | G C |

Practice one last sequence.

G | C | C G | F G |

Follow the chord indications in your book and practice playing the whole accompaniment. The shifts in position may take some additional practice.

KEYBOARD 9

Playing a Three-Part Round

"Tumba" uses three different positions. The fingering at the beginning of each line shows you how your hand should be placed on the keyboard.

Tumba

Hebrew Melody

KEYBOARD 10

Playing a Two-Handed Broken-Chord Accompaniment

Practice each of the positions below. Notice the new position for D_7 of the verse. When you feel comfortable with these broken-chord positions, play the printed accompaniment on the next page. What other ways can you play these broken chords? Try using different order of pitches and different rhythms. Experiment on your own.

Blow the Wind Southerly

Folk Song from Northumbria

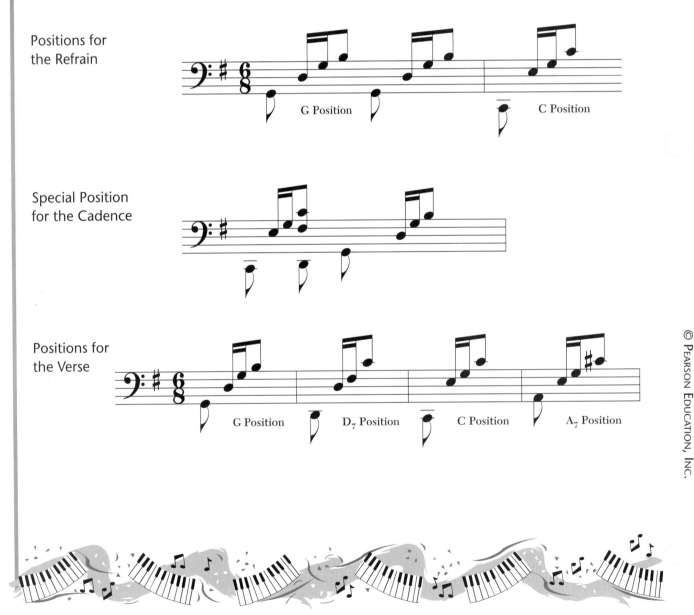

Positions for the Refrain

Special Position for the Cadence

Positions for the Verse

KEYBOARD 10 (CONTINUED)

KEYBOARD 11

Playing a Left-Hand Accompaniment

Practice these different left-hand broken-chord positions. They may all be played with either fingers 5, 2, 1 or 5, 3, 1. Your choice will depend on the size of your hand and the ease of playing.

Am   Em   C   G   F

Accompaniment

Johnny Has Gone for a Soldier

Song of the American Revolution
Collected by John Allison

KEYBOARD 12

Playing an Accompaniment Using Triplets

This accompaniment uses closest position I, IV, and V chords in the key of D major. Use the practice chart and the rhythm chart before playing the accompaniment.

Oh, Watch the Stars

Folk Song from South Carolina

Practice Chart

Rhythm Chart

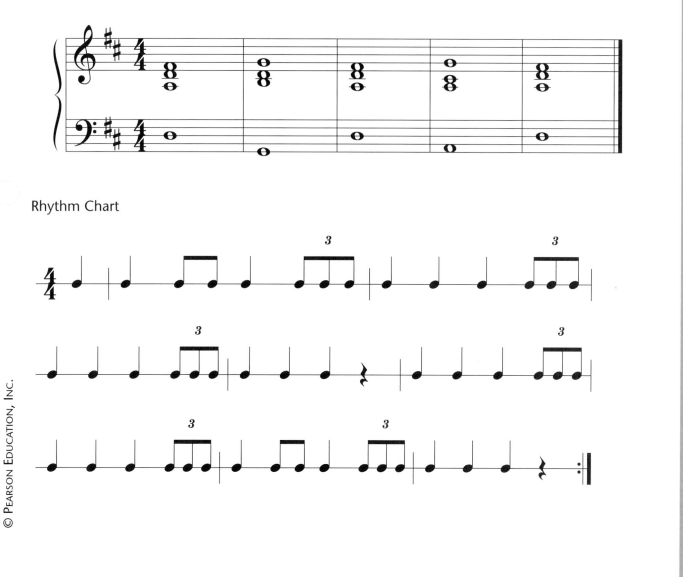

KEYBOARD

Keyboard 12 (continued)

Accompaniment

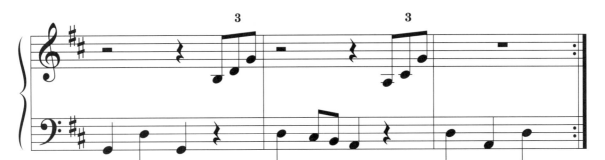

KEYBOARD 13

Playing a Blues Improvisation

Improvising in a blues style is a lot of fun and actually quite easy! Practice the two charts below before you attempt an improvisation. The important thing is to *always* know where the beat is.

Good Mornin', Blues

New Words and New Musical Arrangement
by Huddie Ledbetter

Left-Hand Practice Chart

Right-Hand Practice Chart

A four-bar possibility

Did you swing all of
those eighth notes?

Try a few right-hand four-bar ideas of your own. The beauty of the blues pentascale is that you cannot play a wrong pitch! If you stay with those five pitches, any one you play, no matter what order, will sound good.

When you feel comfortable with the right-hand creating, add the left-hand tritones as whole note values. Below is the chord chart you should follow. Remember, the right hand can go in any order or any rhythm you like as long as you don't stray from the five pitches of the blues pentascale as shown above.

F	F	F	F
B♭	B♭	F	F
C	B♭	F	F

KEYBOARD 14

Left-Handed Accompaniment in Steady Beat

Play a left-handed accompaniment that keeps a steady beat.

Down By the Riverside

African American Spiritual

Grade 5, Teacher Edition, page 256

KEYBOARD 15

Two-Handed Syncopation

Camptown Races

Words and Music by Stephen Foster

KEYBOARD 16

Rhythmic Accompaniment

¡Qué bonita bandera! (What a Beautiful Banner!)

Folk Song from Puerto Rico

KEYBOARD 17

Broken-Chord Accompaniment

La Jesusita

Folk Song from Mexico

KEYBOARD 18

Another Left-Hand Accompaniment

Cattle Call

Words and Music by Tex Owens

© PEARSON EDUCATION, INC.

KEYBOARD 19

Playing a Tritone Accompaniment

St. Louis Blues

Words and Music by W. C. Handy

Play the tritone right hand and include a walking bass in the left hand.

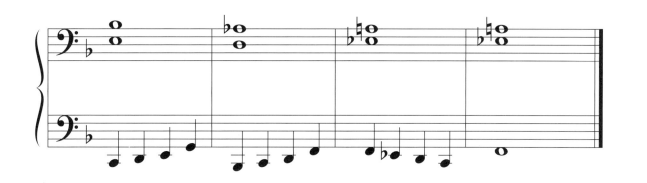

Name ______________________________ Class ______________

KEYBOARD 20

Playing a "Strumming" Accompaniment

This "strumming" style gets its name from the guitar practice of gently playing the pitches in a chord individually. Play the "strumming" accompaniment for "Blowin' in the Wind" based on the chord chart below.

Blowin' in the Wind

Words and Music by Bob Dylan

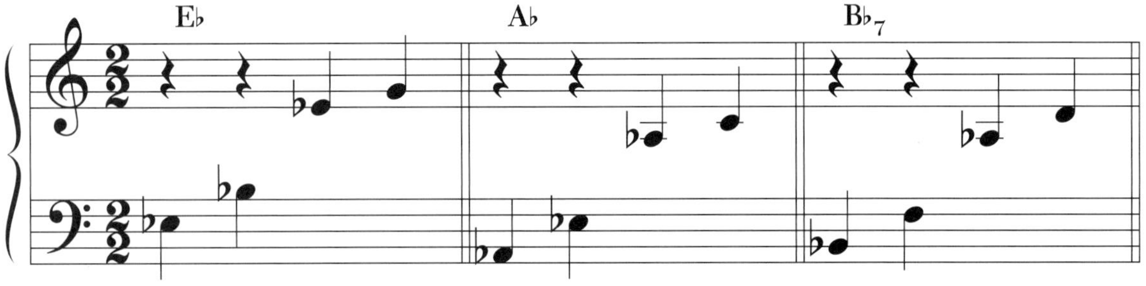

E♭ | A♭ | E♭ | E♭ | E♭ | A♭ | E♭ | B♭7 |

E♭ | A♭ | E♭ | E♭ | E♭ | A♭ | B♭7 | B♭7 |

E♭ | A♭ | E♭ | E♭ | E♭ | A♭ | E♭ | E♭ |

A♭ | B♭7 | E♭ | E♭ | A♭ | B♭7 | E♭ | E♭ |

Playing a Melody in Free Meter

Tap your foot to the rhythm of *"Ríu ríu chíu"* as you count the beats within each measure. The quarter note should remain constant.

Ríu ríu chíu

Sixteenth-Century Carol from Spain

Example:

1	2	3	4	1	2	3	
tap	tap	tap	tap	tap		tap	

1	2	3	1	2	1	2	3	4	5	6
tap			tap	tap	tap		tap			

1	2	3	4	1	2	3	4	
tap	tap	tap	tap	tap		tap	tap	

etc.

Play the melody as written in your Student Text, page 434.

KEYBOARD 22

"Comping" Beneath Scat Syllables

The scat rhythms in "Now's the Time" serve as a unique way to *count* the rhythms of the melody. Have three of your classmates perform four measures of scat rhythms. They may choose to use some of the rhythms from the book or they may create their own.

"Comping" is the practice of playing harmony and, if no bass player is present, walking bass. Practice the one- and two-bar bass lines as well as the right-hand tritone harmonies.

Now's the Time

Music by Charlie Parker
Arranged by Norma Jean Luckey

"Comp" while your classmates perform their scat creations. Follow the order of the chart—four beats to a bar.

F	|B♭	|F	|F		
B♭	|B♭	|F	|F		
C	|B♭	|F	|F	‖

Trade parts and play again!

Grade 5, Teacher Edition, page 444

KEYBOARD **23**

Playing an Introduction and an Interlude

The music below is to be used as both an *introduction* and an *interlude*. The interlude begins in measure 16 immediately after the lyrics *"Ad – dams Fam – i – ly."* Notice that the two patterns used—one beginning on "F", the other beginning on "G"—are sequences. A sequence is a pattern that is repeated at a higher or lower pitch level. Use sequential fingering for an efficient playing—right hand 1, 2, 3, 4 and left hand 4, 3, 2, 1.

The Addams Family

Words and Music by Vic Mizzy

KEYBOARD

KEYBOARD 24

Playing an Ostinato Accompaniment

The following ostinatos outline the Dm, Gm, and A₇ chords.

Oy, Hanuka (O, Chanukah)

Yiddish Folk Song

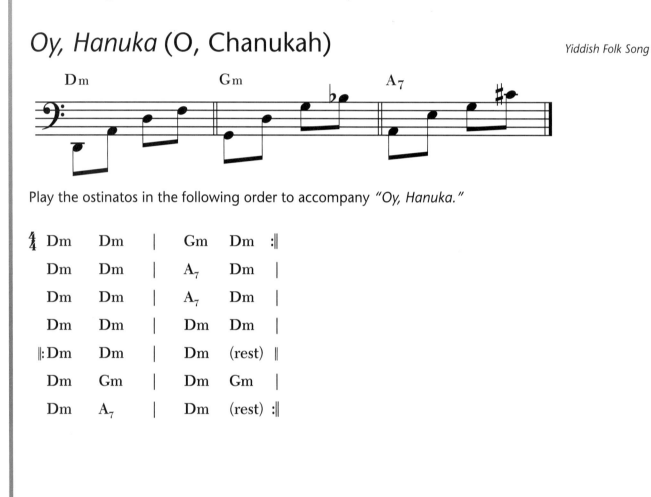

Play the ostinatos in the following order to accompany "Oy, Hanuka."

$\frac{4}{4}$ Dm   Dm | Gm   Dm   :‖

     Dm   Dm | A₇   Dm |

     Dm   Dm | A₇   Dm |

     Dm   Dm | Dm   Dm |

‖: Dm   Dm | Dm   (rest)   ‖

     Dm   Gm | Dm   Gm |

     Dm   A₇ | Dm   (rest)   :‖

RECORDER

Table of Contents

Half-Step Rule in Action—*Laredo* I-2

Choosing Parts—*Bound for South Australia* I-3

Changing Styles—*Morning Has Broken* I-4

Adding Low D and E—*California* I-5

Rhythmic Fun—*Drill, Ye Tarriers* I-6

Playing F and Low C—*A la puerta del cielo* (At the Gate of Heaven) I-7

Feeling Meter in 3—*De colores* I-8

Feeling Meter in 4—*Don't You Hear the Lambs?* I-9

Feeling Meter in 3—*The Ash Grove* I-10

Making Choices—*Wabash Cannon Ball* I-11

Playing a "BAG" Plus Two Song—*Scotland the Brave* I-12

Playing B♭—*Loch Lomond* I-13

Playing a Trill—*Ama-Lama* I-14

Breath Marks—*Blow the Wind Southerly* I-15

Longer Phrases—*Simple Gifts* I-16

Playing in Harmony—*Hound Dog* I-17

Playing with Style—*Oh, Watch the Stars* I-18

What Is a Tie?—*Linstead Market* I-19

Playing a Sequence—*Shady Grove* I-20

Call and Response—*Shenandoah* I-21

Lots of Leaps—*Colorado Trail* I-22

Descending Patterns—*El carite* (The Kingfish) I-23

A "BAG" Song Plus Two—*La Jesusita* I-24

Playing a Swing Song—*Sing, Sing, Sing!* I-25

Feel the Meter in 3—*Cattle Call* I-26

Playing with Style—*Come and Go with Me to That Land* I-27

Changing Meter—*El desembre congelat* (Cold December) I-28

Soprano Recorder Fingerings **I-29**

RECORDER

RECORDER 1

Half-Step Rule in Action

Review the fingering for G♯ and F♯. Remember the half-step rule. Think of the fingering for the note one-half-step higher than the note with the sharp. Skip a finger and then add the next two fingers. Check the fingering chart to see if you have fingered G♯ and F♯ correctly.

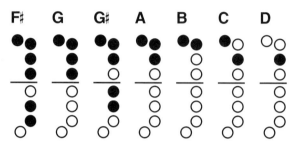

Laredo

Folk Song from Mexico

RECORDER 2

Choosing Parts

This recorder part will give you additional practice reading
G and A. During the verse, play the Call or the Response.
A small group should play the Refrain.

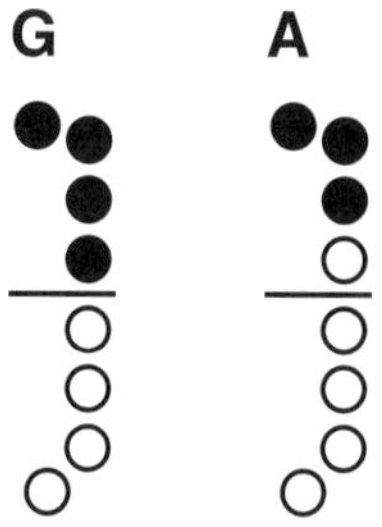

G   A

Bound for South Australia

Sea Shanty

RECORDER

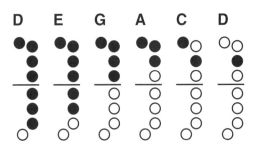

RECORDER 3

Changing Styles

Play this recorder countermelody as others sing this traditional song. Play each phrase in one breath as you blend the recorder sound with the instruments on the recording. The breath marks will help you.

Morning Has Broken

Traditional Gaelic Melody

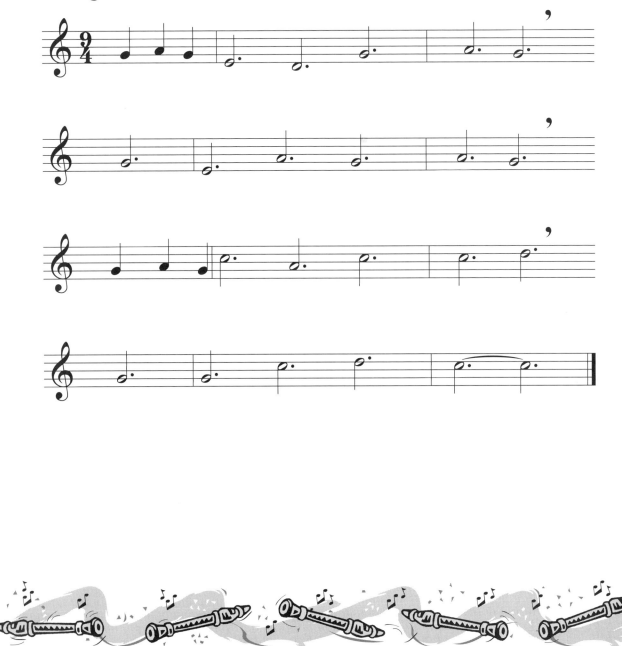

© PEARSON EDUCATION, INC.

RECORDER 4

Adding Low D and E

This recorder part will give you practice reading low D and E. Remember to use very little air when playing notes in the low register. Observe the breath marks (𝄾) as you play.

D   E   A   B

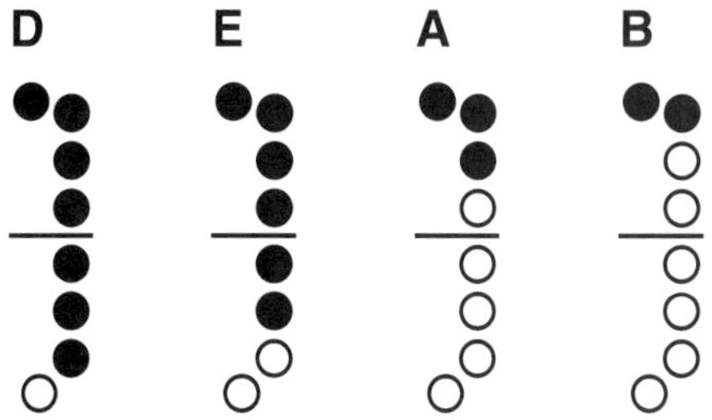

California

Folk Song from the United States

RECORDER

RECORDER 5

Rhythmic Fun

Look at the recorder part below. Notice it contains eighth-
and sixteenth-note rhythms. In order to articulate these
rhythms clearly, make sure you whisper *daah* on each
note. When playing leaps, make sure your fingers are
moving together.

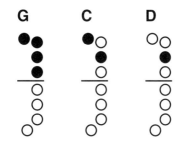

Drill, Ye Tarriers

Words and Music by Thomas Casey

RECORDER 6

Playing F and Low C

Review the fingering for F and low C before playing this countermelody. Check that you are covering the holes on your recorder securely. Notice when you leap from F down to C, or from C up to F, you only have to move one finger. When removing fingers, remember to lift them slightly above the holes.

A la puerta del cielo (At the Gate of Heaven)

Folk Song from Spain

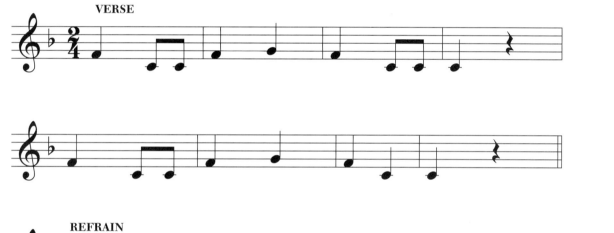

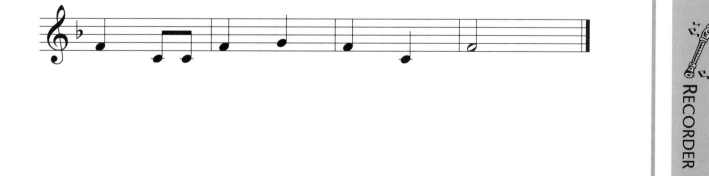

RECORDER

RECORDER 7

Feeling Meter in 3

This recorder countermelody can be played to accompany "De colores." Just like the melody, the beats are grouped in sets of three. Make sure that you hold each dotted half note (𝅗𝅥.) for three beats.

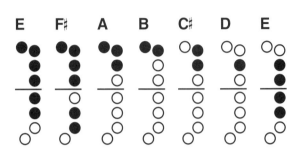

De colores

Folk Song from Mexico

RECORDER 8

Feeling Meter in 4

Review the fingering for D, E, F♯, G, and A. Remember that when you leap from D up to F♯ you only have to lift one finger. Play the countermelody below as others sing the song. The recorder countermelody begins on the first full measure of the melody. Rest during the upbeat.

Don't You Hear the Lambs?

Folk Hymn from the Southern United States

RECORDER 9

Feeling Meter in 3

Play the countermelody below with the recording of "The Ash Grove" to add a second harmony part to the song. On the third and fourth staff, notice the two-note slurs. Only say *daah* on the first of the two slurred notes, so the notes will be connected.

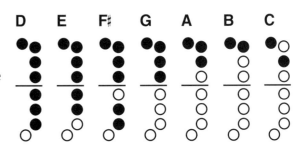

The Ash Grove

Folk Song from Wales

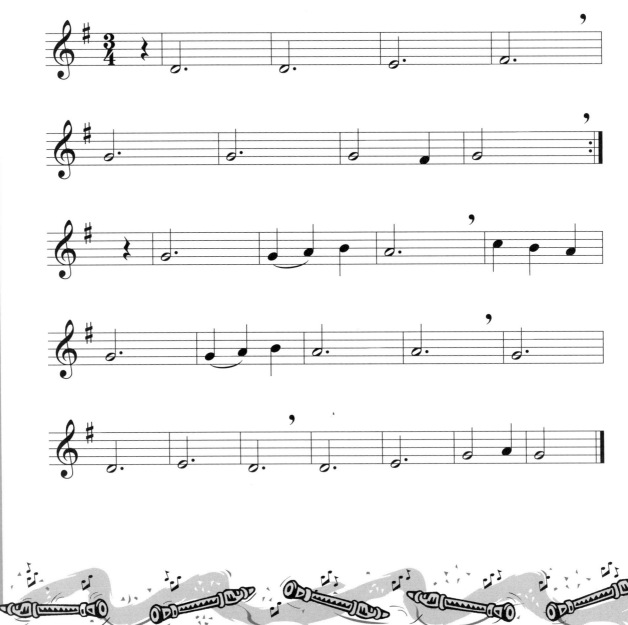

RECORDER 10

Making Choices

Practice saying the rhythm of this countermelody before playing it. Play this countermelody to accompany either the verse or the refrain of the song. Choose when you want to sing and when you want to play.

Wabash Cannon Ball

Traditional

RECORDER

Recorder 11

Playing a "BAG" Plus Two Song

Practice the countermelody below. Notice the rhythm pattern at the beginning of the refrain is found in the song. Remember to whisper *daah* in the style of the music.

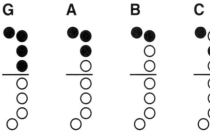

Scotland the Brave

Traditional Melody from Scotland

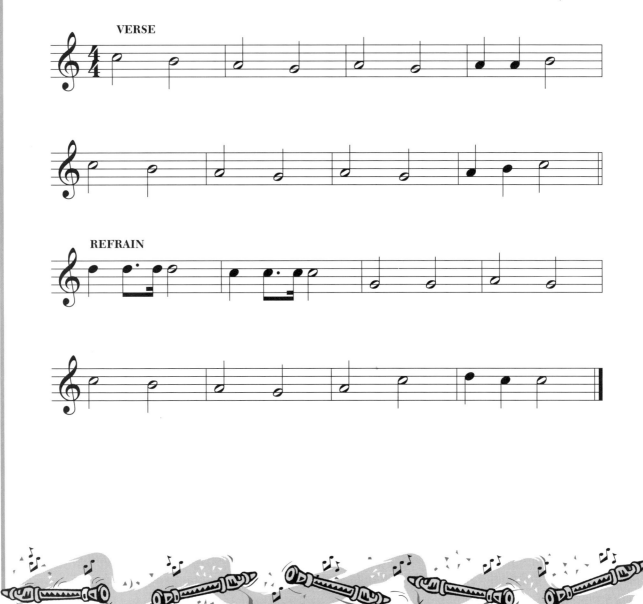

RECORDER 12

Playing B♭

Review the fingering for B♭ by using the half-step rule. Remember to think of the fingering for B, then skip a hole and add the next two fingers. You are now playing B♭. Play this countermelody to accompany "Loch Lomond."

C D E F A B♭

Loch Lomond

Folk Song from Scotland

VERSE

REFRAIN

RECORDER

RECORDER 13

Playing a Trill

Review the notes for A, B♭, and C. Then play the following recorder part to accompany "Ama-Lama."

Try playing a trill on C during the B section and *Coda.* To play the trill, move your left thumb on and off the hole rapidly to play C to D. Be sure to sustain your breath during the trill. Tongue only on the C's in measures 1 and 3 of the B section.

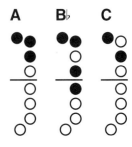

Ama-Lama

Traditional

RECORDER 14

Breath Marks

As you play the countermelody below, observe the breath marks (ʾ). Breath marks separate musical ideas in the same way that commas and periods separate written ideas. Breathe only between phrases.

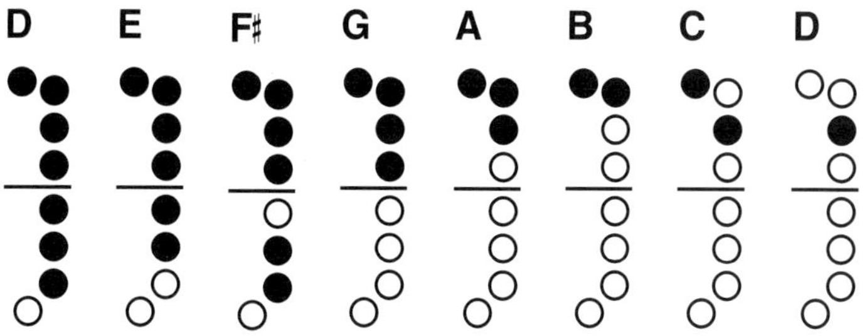

D E F♯ G A B C D

Blow the Wind Southerly

Folk Song from Northumbria

REFRAIN

Fine

VERSE

D.C. al Fine

RECORDER

RECORDER 15

Longer Phrases

Notice that the breath marks in this song occur at the end of each four-measure phrase. Think through the long phrases as you play this countermelody. Whisper *daah* gently as you conserve your breath for the entire phrase.

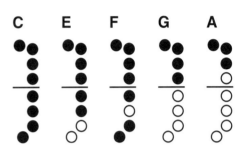

C E F G A

Simple Gifts

Shaker Song

Grade 5, Teacher Edition, page 184

RECORDER 16

Playing in Harmony

Practice both countermelodies for "Hound Dog" on your recorder. With a friend, decide who will play countermelody 1 and who will play countermelody 2. Listen to both parts as you play in harmony.

Hound Dog

Words and Music by Jerry Leiber and Mike Stoller

RECORDER 17

Playing with Style

Practice fingering the notes D, E, F♯, G, and A before playing the countermelody below. Make sure you articulate each eighth note clearly as you play. Play with the recording of this song in the style of the music.

Oh, Watch the Stars

Folk Song from South Carolina

Grade 5, Teacher Edition, page 216

RECORDER 18

What Is a Tie?

Look at the countermelody below and notice that there are four phrases. Compare the phrases and identify which are the same and which are different. Observe the tied notes at the beginning of phrase one and two.

Linstead Market

Calypso Song from Jamaica

RECORDER 19

Playing Sequences

Melodic sequence is a pattern of pitches that is repeated at a higher or lower pitch level. Identify the melodic sequence in the first and third lines of the following recorder part. Then play the part to accompany "Shady Grove."

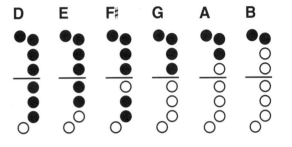

Shady Grove

Folk Song from the United States

*Advanced students may be invited to perform these notes.

Grade 5, Teacher Edition, page 260

© PEARSON EDUCATION, INC.

RECORDER 20

Call and Response

Play this countermelody with friends. Choose who will play the Call and who will play the Response, then switch parts. Whisper *daah* in the style of the music as you play.

D E F♯ G A

Shenandoah

Capstan Sea Shanty

RECORDER

RECORDER 21

Lots of Leaps

When playing leaps, remember to move your fingers together. Practice this song slowly, whispering *daah* on each note. Compare the first and third phrase, then compare the second and fourth phrase. How are they the same or different?

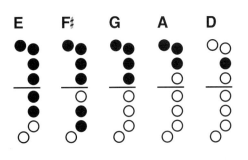

Colorado Trail

Cowboy Song

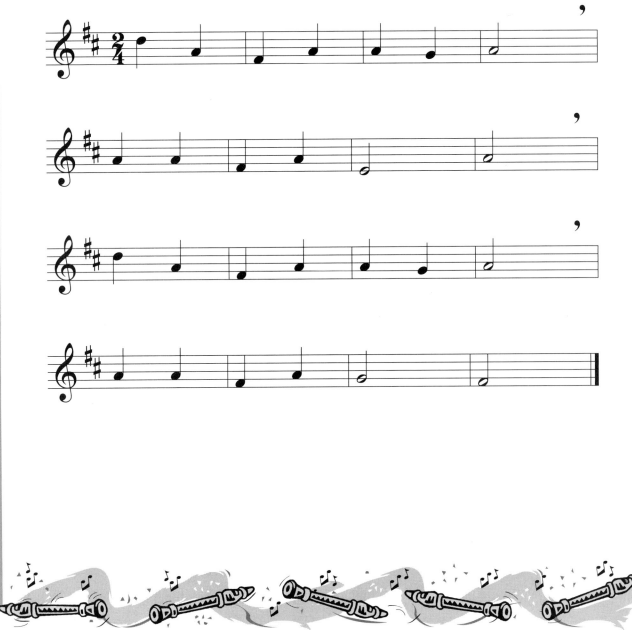

Grade 5, Teacher Edition, page 276

RECORDER 22

Descending Patterns

Play a descending C scale (C, B, A, G, F, E, D, C) on your recorder. Then begin with G and play the last five notes of the C scale, and begin on F and play the last four notes of the C scale. The countermelody below uses variations of both of these descending patterns. Play it during the verse of *"El carite."*

Folk Song from Venezuela

El carite (The Kingfish)

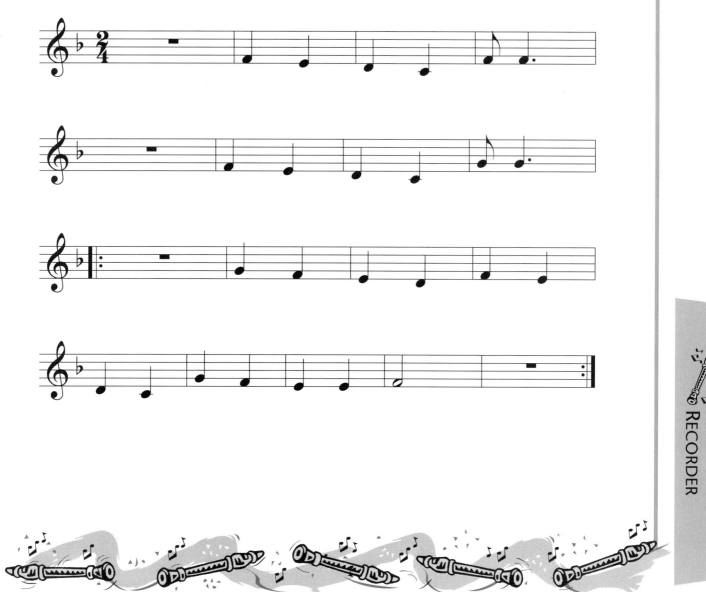

RECORDER

RECORDER 23

A "BAG" Song Plus Two

This countermelody for the verse of *"La Jesusita"* includes notes that are fingered only with the left hand. Make sure your right hand is still in the correct position with the right thumb behind the fourth and fifth holes and fingers curved slightly above holes four through seven.

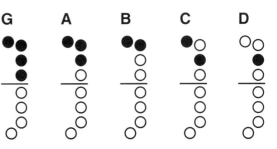

La Jesusita

Folk Song from Mexico

RECORDER 24

Playing a Swing Song

Look at the recorder part below. As you read this part, make sure you observe the repeat signs. Say *daah* in the style of the music as you play this swing tune.

Sing, Sing, Sing!

Words and Music by Louis Prima

Recorder 25

Feel the Meter in 3

Feel the beats grouped in sets of three as you play this countermelody. During the verse, there are many dotted half notes (𝅗𝅥.). Say *daah* on the first beat and continue the flow of air for all three beats.

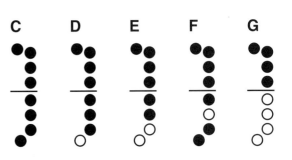

Cattle Call

Words and Music by Tex Owens

Grade 5, Teacher Edition, page 344

RECORDER 26

Playing with Style

After you can play the countermelody below, play the recorder along with the recorded version of the song. Feel the beat and whisper *daah* in the style of the music as you play.

Come and Go with Me to That Land

African American Spiritual

RECORDER 27

Changing Meter

Play the countermelody below to accompany *"El desembre congelat."* Notice that the time signature changes for one measure. Continue to feel the quarter note pulse even when the meter changes.

El desembre congelat (Cold December)

Fifteenth-Century Melody from Catalonia

© PEARSON EDUCATION, INC.

Grade 5, Teacher Edition, page 473

RECORDER 28

Soprano Recorder Fingerings

Practice fingering the notes from lowest to highest.

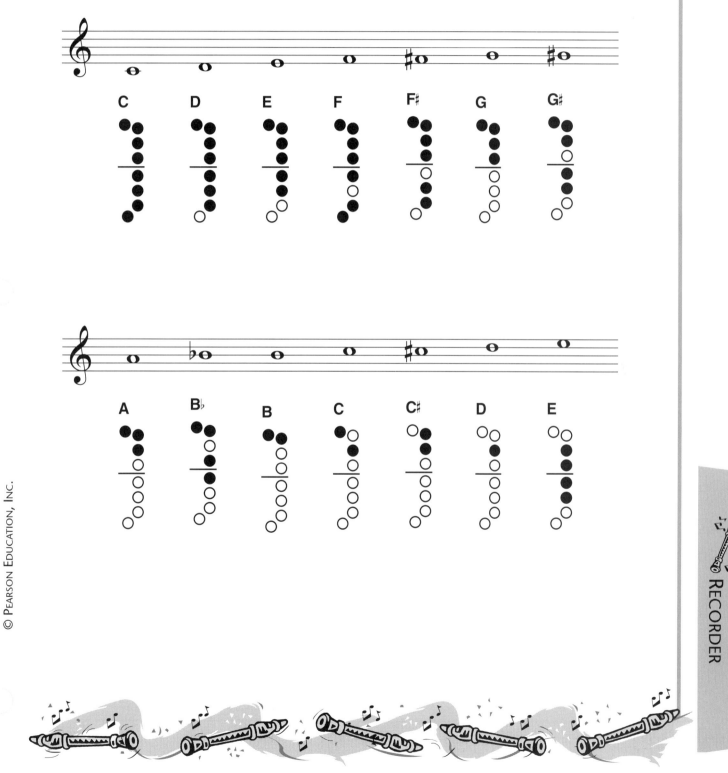

Teacher Notes

ACTIVITY MASTERS

Table of Contents

A Letter to Home (English) J-2

A Letter to Home (Spanish) J-3

Instrument Identification J-4

A Dynamic Performance J-5

Crossword Puzzle 1 . . . . J-6

Exercise in Form J-7

Scale Identification J-8

Crossword Puzzle 2 . . . . J-9

American Music J-10

Twentieth-Century Styles J-11

Song Research J-12

Keyboard Diagram ***J-13***

Bell Diagram ***J-14***

Autoharp Diagram ***J-15***

Activity Masters Answer Key ***J-16***

ACTIVITY MASTER 1

A Letter to Home

This year, your child will be participating in a music class designed to foster lifelong appreciation of music through active music making. The sequenced music instruction will help your child develop musical skills and understanding, using music of various styles from the United States and around the world. In addition to developing specific musical skills, your child's studies in other areas will be enhanced by instruction that links concepts across the curriculum.

Your child will also have opportunities to participate in theme-based music making. Some possible themes include American music, world music, friends, families, self-esteem, animals, ecology, storytelling, choral singing, seasons, and celebrations. Your child may also be involved in classroom and/or school-wide performances, and you will be invited to attend or volunteer to assist with these performances.

You can also reinforce your child's music learning at home. Consider listening to music together and talking about it. Ask your child to share songs learned in music class. Attend local concerts to help foster appropriate audience behavior. These experiences will help make music meaningful at school, at home, and in the community.

Sincerely,

ACTIVITY MASTER 2

Una Carta al Hogar

Este año, su niño(a) tomará parte en una clase de música que le ayudará a adquirir una apreciación de música durante toda la vida mediante su participación en actividades musicales. La instrucción de música, que está estructurada en una secuencia lógica, le ayudará a su niño(a) a desarrollar destrezas y conocimientos musicales, al experimentar distintos estilos de música de los Estados Unidos y de todas partes del mundo. Además del desarrollo de destrezas musicales, su niño(a) mejorará en los otros campos de estudio porque la instrucción relaciona conceptos provenientes de todo el plan de estudios.

Su niño(a) también tendrá oportunidades de tomar parte en actividades musicales basadas en un tema. Entre estos temas hay música americana, música mundial, amigos, familias, auto-estima, animales, ecología, cuentos, canto coral, estaciones y celebraciones. Tal vez su niño(a) pueda estar envuelto en actuaciones en la clase y/o para toda la escuela, y se le invitará a usted(es) a asistir o a ayudar con estas actuaciones como voluntario(a). Usted(es) también puede(n) reforzar en casa el aprendizaje de música de su niño(a). Consideren escuchar a música juntos y después hablar sobre lo que oyeron. Pídale a su niño(a) que comparta con usted(es) las canciones que ha aprendido en la clase de música. Llévelo(la) a conciertos de la zona para ayudarle a experimentar en la audiencia conducta apropiada. Todo esto ayudará a hacer que la música sea una experiencia significativa para su niño(a) en la escuela, en casa y en la comunidad.

Sinceramente,

ACTIVITY MASTER 3

Instrument Identification

Study the pictures of the instruments on page 65 in your music textbook.
Then answer these questions.

1. Which of these instruments are struck with a mallet? _____

2. Which are played with a pair of wooden sticks? _____

3. Which percussion instruments are tuned to specific pitches?

_____

4. Which percussion instruments are nonpitched? _____

5. Which are made of metal? _____

6. Which instruments are usually heard in an American marching band?

_____

7. Which is capable of making the loudest sound? _____

8. Which are drums usually played in an orchestra? _____

9. Which instruments would you pick to sound like horses' hooves on

cobblestones? _____

Write words that describe the sound of three of these instruments.

1. _____   _____
    Name of instrument   Words that describe its sound

2. _____   _____
    Name of instrument   Words that describe its sound

3. _____   _____
    Name of instrument   Words that describe its sound

ACTIVITY MASTER 4

A Dynamic Performance

Review the dynamic markings below. Then join some friends and perform the sound piece.
Perform each sound for four beats.

pp	*(pianissimo)*	very soft
p	*(piano)*	soft
mp	*(mezzo piano)*	medium soft
mf	*(mezzo forte)*	medium loud
f	*(forte)*	loud
ff	*(fortissimo)*	very loud

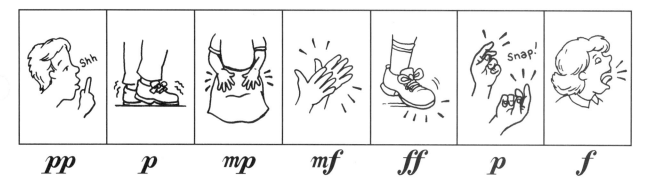

| ***pp*** | ***p*** | ***mp*** | ***mf*** | ***ff*** | ***p*** | ***f*** |

Create your own sound piece. Notate it so that it can be performed by your classmates. Write
your dynamic marks under the various sounds.

ACTIVITY MASTER 5

Crossword Puzzle 1

ABA	*dundun*	*mambo*	partner	Rodgers
Berlin	dynamics	*marcato*	pentatonic	*shakuhachi*
canon	Ellis	Marine	percussion	syncopation
contour	Estefan	meter	*piano*	time
crescendo	*fortissimo*	motive	polyphonic	verse
descant	Leonard	ostinato	refrain	voice

Across

2. Music based on a five-tone scale (p. 24)
7. The type of form where the first and last sections are the same. The middle section is different. (p. 100)
8. Very loud (p. 8)
10. A Japanese flute made of bamboo (p. 112)
11. A rhythm pattern (p. 12)
12. The degrees of loudness and softness in sounds (p. 6)
13. Gradually get louder (p. 46)
16. The first name of the American composer who wrote the music for the Broadway hit show "West Side Story" (p. 9)
18. The shape of a melody (p. 29)
19. Two or more songs sung at the same time to create harmony are called _____ songs (p. 69)
22. Stressed or accented (p. 87)
25. Another melody that decorates the main tune, usually placed above the main melody (p. 114)
26. The meter symbol at the beginning of a song is called a ____ signature (p. 10)
27. Your own instrument (p. 28)
28. The Immigration Museum is located on _____ Island (p. 57)
29. This man could not read music but still composed over 1,500 songs (p. 74)

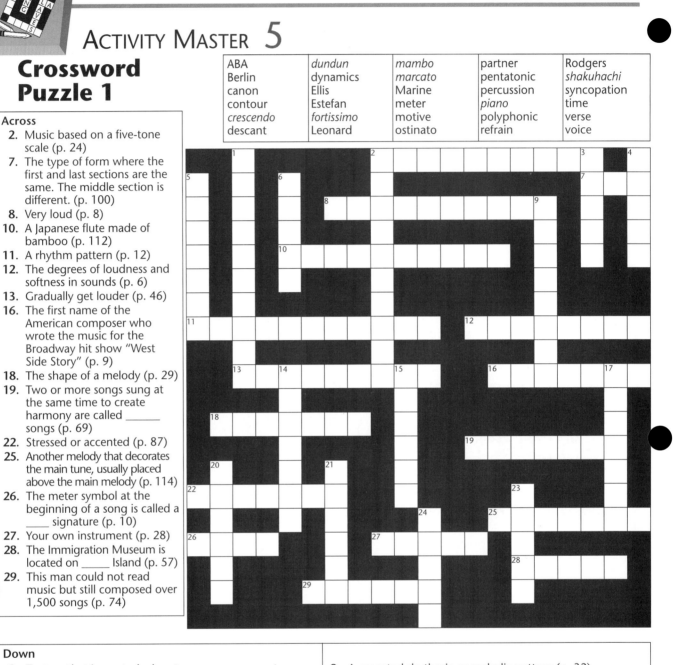

Down

1. Texture that is created when two or more separate melodies are sung or played together (p. 73)
2. A ____ instrument is played by scraping, striking, or shaking (p. 64)
3. A form of music in which two or more voices sing the same melody but begin at different times (p. 158)
4. This dance originated in Cuba (p. 9)
5. He composed the music and Hammerstein wrote the lyrics for many Broadway shows (p. 39)
6. The section of a song that is sung before the refrain (p. 56)
9. A repeated rhythmic or melodic pattern (p. 32)
14. This Latin performer has won two Grammy awards (p. 8)
15. This is a name of an African drum (p. 66)
17. Part of the song that repeats, using the same melody and words (p. 56)
20. The official band of the President of the United States (p. 79)
21. A short musical fragment (p. 59)
23. The way beats of a measure are grouped (p. 50)
24. Soft (p. 8)

ACTIVITY MASTER 6

An Exercise in Form

Identify the form that these letters represent. Draw the B and C sections.

A   **B**   **A**   **C**   **A**

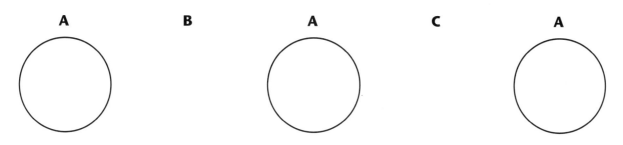

The picture in the first box below represents a theme. Draw two variations on this theme.

Create a poem in AABA form. If you need more room, use the other side of this paper. Your poem does not have to rhyme.

A _____

A _____

B _____

A _____

Create a movement piece in any of the above forms. Use the other side of the paper if you need more room.

_____

_____

_____

ACTIVITY MASTER 7

Scale Identification

These are four scales that you have studied. Each has a note that is missing. Read the name of the scale and notate the missing pitch on the staff.

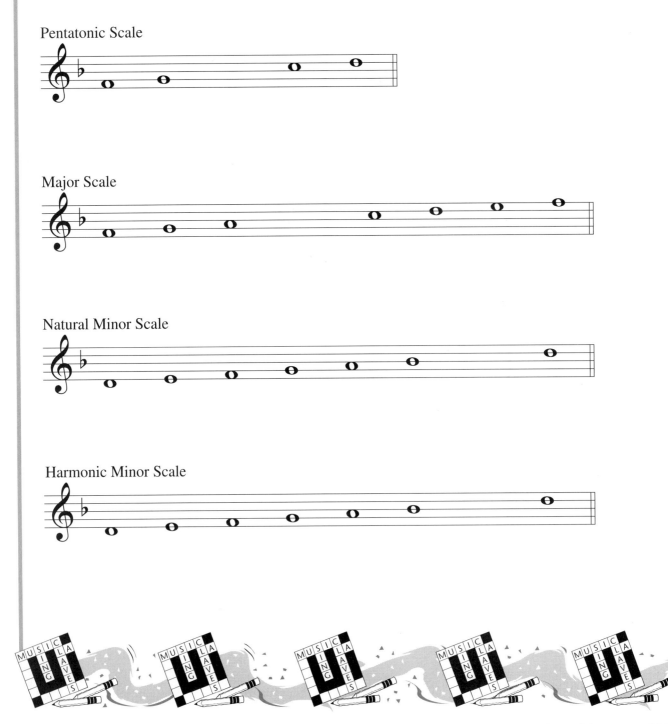

Pentatonic Scale

Major Scale

Natural Minor Scale

Harmonic Minor Scale

Grade 5, Teacher Edition, page 190

ACTIVITY MASTER 8
Crossword Puzzle 2

accent	compound	Gilmore	Rich	*taiko*
accidental	conga	harpsichord	rondo	triplet
bagpipes	Copland	Jackson	round	upbeats
Beatles	diatonic	*kantele*	sequence	Valens
calypso	drum	minor	slur	variations
	Elvis			

Across

2. This mark indicates that a note should be sung or played with more emphasis than the other notes (p. 173)

5. A follow-the-leader process in which all sing the same melody but start at different times (p. 160)

7. A melodic ___ is a pattern of pitches that is repeated at a higher or lower pitch level (p. 149)

9. Tall drums with high, medium, and low pitches (p. 156)

11. A Scottish instrument (p. 138)

13. A mark to indicate that a syllable is sung on more than one pitch (p. 170)

14. A musical form in which the first section always returns (p. 142)

16. When the beat is subdivided into groups of three, it is called ____ meter (p. 175)

17. This sign is used to show an altered pitch (p. 191)

18. The natural ___ scale uses the same notes as the major scale, but they're arranged in a different pattern of whole steps and half steps (p. 188)

22. The king of rock 'n' roll (p. 212)

23. The true queen of spiritual singers (p. 193)

24. The most famous English pop group of all (p. 208)

25. A keyboard string instrument (p. 197)

26. One of the first famous Hispanic rock stars (p. 130)

Down

1. These are sometimes called "weak" beats (p. 132)

3. The rhythm symbol to show three even sounds on a beat in a simple meter (p. 217)

4. This instrument has been in existence for at least 6,000 years (p. 154)

6. Means "big drum" in Japanese (p. 156)

8. He was nicknamed "Traps, the Drum Wonder" (p. 155)

10. He won a Pulitzer Prize for a ballet he wrote (p. 186)

12. This scale uses seven different notes (p. 146)

15. Theme and ____ is a musical form in which each section is a modification of the initial theme (p. 183)

16. A type of song from Jamaica (p. 200)

20. The name of a Union army bandmaster (p. 181)

21. A small string instrument that is a national symbol of Finland (p. 199)

ACTIVITY MASTER 9

American Music

Read Unit 7 in your music textbook to find the answers to these questions about American music.

1. American spirituals were written by _____.

2. What early American song was originally written with shaped notes?

   _____

3. What group of workers sang sea shantys? _____

4. **a)** Who was one of America's best-liked composers of popular
      songs in the nineteenth century?

      _____

   b) What area of America were most of his songs about?

      _____

5. What types of songs are sung to promote one's enthusiasm for a country?

   _____

6. Name two famous American folk singers.

   _____   _____

7. Look at the lyrics to "Woke Up This Morning." What are they about?

   _____

8. Why do you think people write and sing songs such as "If I Had a Hammer"
   and "Woke Up This Morning?"

   _____

   _____

© PEARSON EDUCATION, INC.

Name _____ Class _____

ACTIVITY MASTER 10

Twentieth-Century Styles

Answer the questions below.

1. Who was one of the greatest ragtime composers? _____

2. Most rags were written for what instrument? _____

3. What do you like most about ragtime? _____

4. What kind of music did big bands play? _____

5. In what years was big band music most popular (1920s, 1930s, 1940s)? _____

6. Name the person who had one of the most popular big bands.

_____

7. What is scat singing? _____

_____

8. Name a famous jazz scat singer of the twentieth century. _____

_____

9. Where is the "home" of country music? _____

_____

10. How many different chords are usually found in the blues? _____

11. What is improvisation? _____

_____

12. What was the name of the first rock 'n' roll band? _____

_____

ACTIVITY MASTER 11

Song Research

Examine the songs in Unit 10 of your music textbook. Look at the definitions below. Select one song that contains a symbol or word that matches the definition. Write its title in the blank. Include the page where it can be found. Exchange papers with your neighbor to check your answers.

1. There are six beats in a measure and an eighth note gets one beat.

_____ _____
Song Title   Page

2. Go back to the beginning and sing until you see the word *fine.*

_____ _____
Song Title   Page

3. Go back to the beginning and sing until you come to the second ending. Skip ending number one when you repeat.

_____ _____
Song Title   Page

4. Repeat this part of the song without change after each verse.

_____ _____
Song Title   Page

5. Identify an example of syncopation.

_____ _____
Song Title   Page

6. Identify an example of a silent beat.

_____ _____
Song Title   Page

7. Identify a song based on a five-note scale.

_____ _____
Song Title   Page

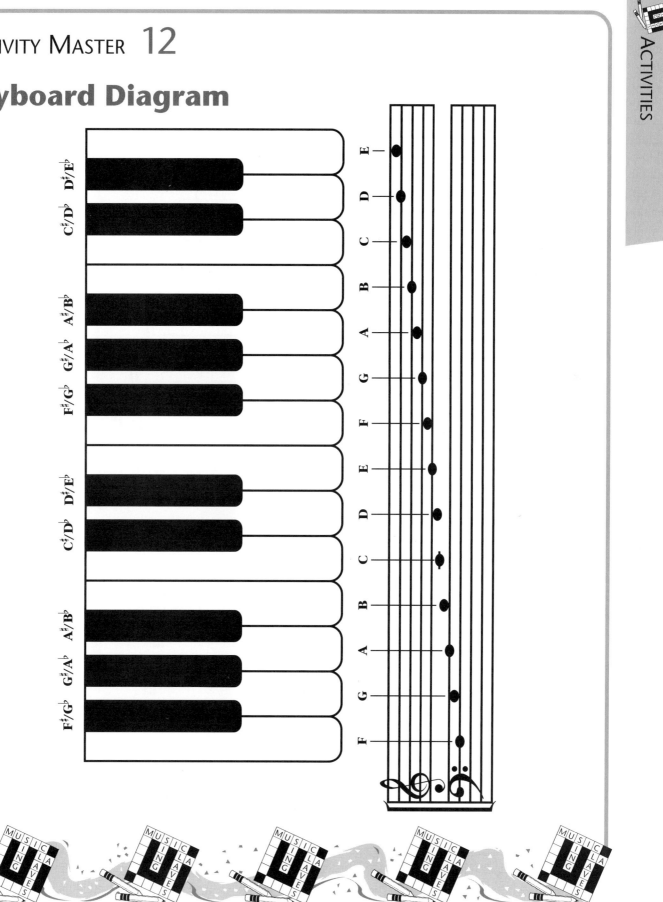

ACTIVITY MASTER 12

Keyboard Diagram

ACTIVITY MASTER 13

Bell Diagram

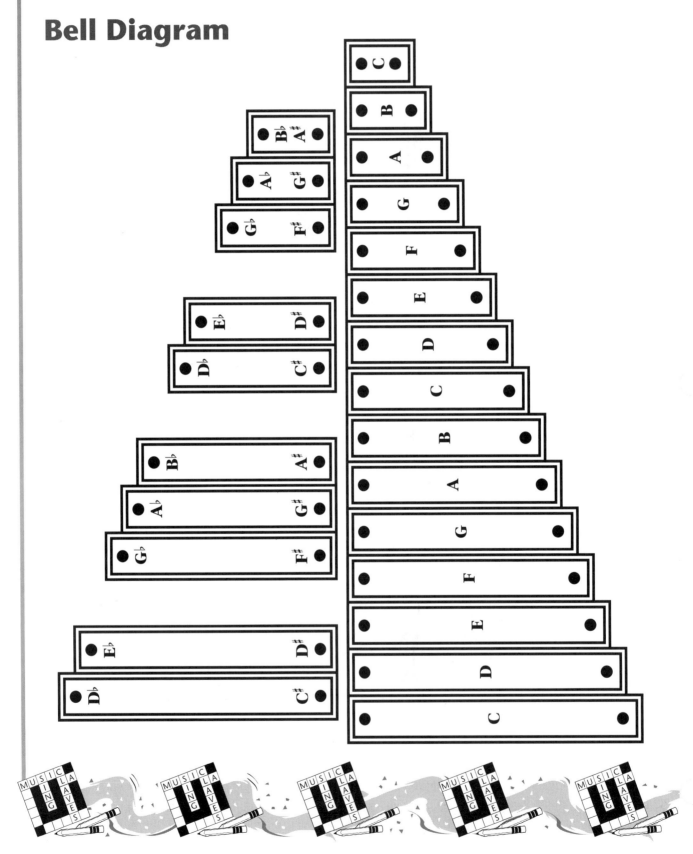

ACTIVITY MASTER 14

Autoharp Diagram

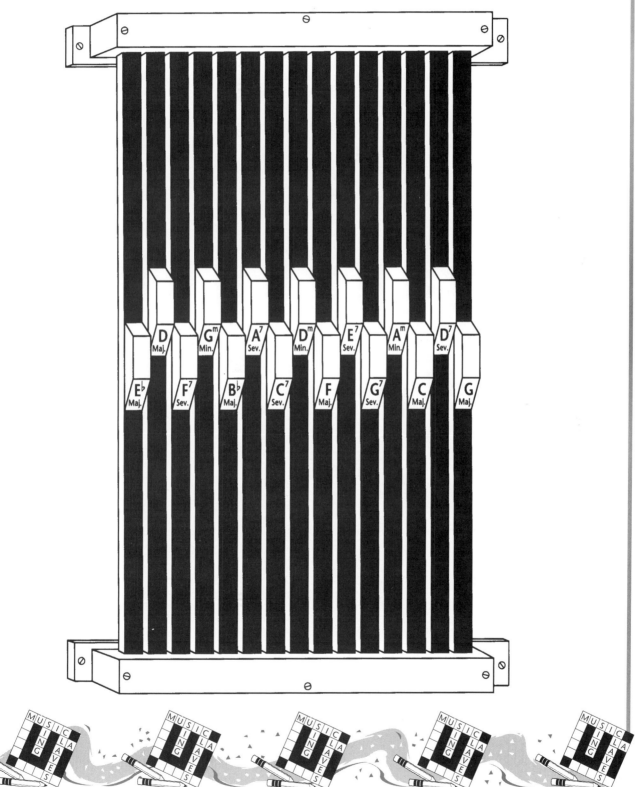

ACTIVITY MASTER ANSWER KEY

Activity Master 3: Instrument Identification

1. xylophone, timpani, and marimba
2. snare drum, cymbals
3. timpani, bells, xylophone, marimba
4. cymbals, triangle, claves, shaker, woodblock, gong, bass drum, tambourine
5. cymbals, snare drum, triangle, bells, gong
6. cymbals, snare drum, bass drum
7. snare drum
8. timpani
9. woodblock, claves
10. Answers will vary.
11. Answers will vary.
12. Answers will vary.

Activity Master 5: Crossword Puzzle 1

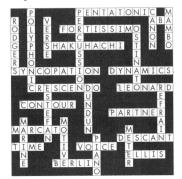

Activity Master 7: Scale Identification

Pentatonic Scale

A

Major Scale

B♭

Natural Minor Scale

C

Harmonic Minor Scale

C♯

Activity Master 8: Crossword Puzzle 2

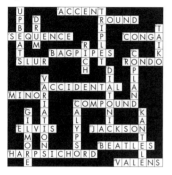

Activity Master 9: American Music

1. European Americans and enslaved African Americans
2. "Amazing Grace"
3. sailors
4. **a.** Stephen Collins Foster
   b. The South
5. patriotic songs
6. Woody Guthrie and Pete Seeger
7. freedom and equality
8. Answers will vary.

Activity Master 11: Twentieth-Century Styles

1. Scott Joplin
2. piano
3. Answers will vary.
4. swing
5. 1930s
6. Glenn Miller
7. Scat is a style of singing in which syllables are used instead of words.
8. Ella Fitzgerald
9. The Grand Ole Opry in Nashville, Tennessee
10. 3 chords
11. Improvisation is a style in which the performer makes up music while playing or singing.
12. Bill Haley and the Comets

Activity Master 12: Song Research

1. *"Río, río"* p. 370
2. *"Zum gali gali"* p. 401
3. "Somewhere Out There" p. 368
4. "Blowin' in the Wind" p. 382
5. "A World of Difference" p. 386
6. "Turn, Turn, Turn" p. 378
7. "Zuni Sunrise Call" p. 396

Teacher Notes

Art Credits

Reading
All art Burgandy Beam.

Activity Master
J-5, Linda Howard Bittner; J-7, Preface.

Orff icons
All art Tony Nuccio.

Signing
All art Burgandy Beam.

Acknowledgments

Credits and appreciation are due publishers and copyright owners for use of the following:

A-4: "Éliza Kongo" from Brown Girl in the Ring by Alan Lomax. Copyright © 1997 by Alan Lomax. Pantheon Books. **A-X:** "La Ciudad de Juaja" (The City Of Juaja), English words by Ruth De Cesare, John Donald Robb Archives of Southwestern Music, College of Fine Arts, University of New Mexico. Used by permission of John Donald Robb Trust. **A-9:** "Ye jaliya da" a folk song from West Africa. Used by permission, DWADD. **A-15:** "Jo'ashila" (Walking Together) Traditional Navajo song from Roots and Branches. Courtesy World Music Press. **A-16:** "La bamba" adapted and arranged by Richie Valens. © 1958 (Renewed) Picture Our Music. WARNER BROS. PUBLICATIONS U.S. INC., Miami, FL 33014. **A-27:** "Tzena, tzena, tzena" English lyrics by Mitchell Parish (with one line altered by Pete Seeger), music and original lyrics by Issachar Miron. © 1950 (Renewed) EMI Mills Music, Inc. All Rights Reserved. Used by Permission. WARNER BROS. PUBLICATIONS U.S. INC., Miami, FL 33014. **A-44:** "O Desayo" arranged by Elliot A. Levine, edited by Henry H. Leck, 1995. Copyright Transferred 2000, Colla Voce Music, Inc., 4600 Sunset Avenue, #83, Indianapolis, IN 46208. Reprinted by permission of Colla Voce Music, Inc. **A-44:** "Uno, dos y tres" Words and Music by Rafael Ortiz. Arrangement © 2002 Carlos Abril/World Music Press. **A-46:** "Hine mah tov" Music by M. Jacobson. Arranged by Henry Leck. Copyright © 1996 by Colla Voce Music. Reprinted by permission of Colla Voce Music, Inc. **A-49:** "Quâ câu gió bay" (The Wind on the Bridge) folk song from Vietnam, as sung by Phong Nguyen, from Roots and Branches: A Legacy of Multicultural Music for Children, © 1994. World Music Press. Used by Permission. **A-50:** "Oy, Hanuka" English from The Gateway to Jewish Songs, collected and translated by Judith Eisenstein. Behrmann's Book House, Inc., New York, NY. Yiddish version: from The New Jewish Songbook, compiled and edited by Harry Coopersmith. Copyright © 1965 Harry Coopersmith. Published by Behrman House, Inc. **A-53:** "El desembre congelat" (Cold December) from The International Book of Christmas Carols, © 1963 Walton Music Corp. Used by permission. **D-16:** "Wabash Cannon Ball" © 1988 Silver Burdett Ginn. **D-28:** "Oh, Watch the Stars" from Folk Songs North America Sings by Richard Johnston. 1984 by Caveat Music Publishing Ltd., copyright assigned 1988 to G. Ricordi & Co. (Canada) Ltd. **D-28:** "Don't You Hear the Lambs?" from Folk Songs North America Sings by Richard Johnston. 1984 by Caveat Music Publishing Ltd., copyright assigned 1988 to G Ricordi & Co. (Canada) Ltd. **E-11:** "Don't You Hear the Lambs?" from Folk Songs North America Sings by Richard Johnston. 1984 by Caveat Music Publishing Ltd., copyright assigned 1988 to G Ricordi & Co. (Canada) Ltd. **E-14:** "Wabash Cannon Ball" © 1988 Silver Burdett Ginn. **E-15:** "Scotland the Brave" Words and music by James Hanley. 1952 (Renewed) Kerrs Music Corp. Ltd. WARNER BROS. PUBLICATIONS U.S. INC., Miami, FL. 33014. **E-17:** "Autumn Canon" Words by Sean Deibler, Music by Lajos Bardos. BMG Music Publishing. **E-20:** "Johnny Has Gone for a Soldier," Collected by John Allison. McCarthy, Fingar, Donovan, Drazen & Smith, LLP. **E-22:** "Oh, Watch the Stars" from Folk Songs North America Sings by Richard Johnston. 1984 by Caveat Music Publishing Ltd., copyright assigned 1988 to G. Ricordi & Co. (Canada) Ltd. **E-23:** "Old Abram Brown" from Friday Afternoons, Music by Benjamin Britten, Words from "Tom Tiddler's Ground" by Walter de la Mare. Copyright 1936 by Boosey & Co. Ltd. **E-24:** "The Greenland Whale Fishery," from Folk Songs North America Sings by Richard Johnston. 1984 by Caveat Music Publishing Ltd., copyright assigned 1988 to G. Ricordi & Co. (Canada) Ltd. **E-25:** "Connemara Lullaby" from Music for Children, Vol. 4, by Carl Orff and Gunild Keetman. © 1966 by Schott Musik. **F-2:** "Morning Comes Early" Slovak Folk Song. ORFF accompaniment © 2002 Pearson Education, Inc. **F-4:** "Arirang" Folk Song from Korea. ORFF ORFF accompaniment © 2002 Pearson Education, Inc. **F-5:** "I Love the Mountains" Folk Song. ORFF accompaniment © 2002 Pearson Education, Inc. **F-6:** "Drill, Ye Tarriers" Words and Music by Thomas Casey. ORFF accompaniment © 2002 Pearson Education, Inc. **F-9:** "De colores" Folk Song from Mexico. ORFF accompaniment © 2002 Pearson Education, Inc. **F-12:** "Joshua Fought the Battle of Jericho" African American Spiritual. ORFF accompaniment © 2002 Pearson Education, Inc. **F-14:** "Dundai" Folk Song from Israel. ORFF accompaniment © 2002 Pearson Education, Inc. **F-x:** "Roll On, Columbia" Words by Woody Guthrie. Music based on GOODNIGHT, IRENE by Huddie Ledbetter and John A. Lomax. TRO- © Copyright 1936 (Renewed) 1957 (Renewed) and 1963 (Renewed) Ludlow Music, Inc., New York, NY. ORFF accompaniment by Pearson Education, Inc. **F-17:** "This Land Is Your Land" Words and Music by Woody Guthrie. TRO- © Copyright 1956 (Renewed) 1958 (Renewed) 1970 (Renewed) Ludlow Music, Inc., New York, NY. ORFF accompaniment by Pearson Education, Inc. **F-18:** "Wabash Cannon Ball" © 1988 Silver Burdett Ginn. ORFF accompaniment © 2002 Pearson Education, Inc. **F-19:** "Autumn Canon" Words by Sean Deibler, Music by Lajos Bardos. BMG Music Publishing. ORFF accompaniment by Pearson Education, Inc. **F-20:** "Las estrellitas del cielo" Folk Song from Spain. ORFF accompaniment © 2002 Pearson Education, Inc. **F-21:** "Don Alfonso" Folk Song from Spain. ORFF accompaniment © 2002 Pearson Education, Inc. **F-22:** "Blow the Wind Southerly" Folk Song from Northumbria. ORFF accompaniment © 2002 Pearson Education, Inc. **F-24:** "Pat Works on the Railway" Arrangement © 2002 Pearson Education, Inc. ORFF accompaniment by Pearson Education, Inc. **F-26:** "Mango Walk" Calypso Song from Jamaica. ORFF accompaniment © 2002 Pearson Education, Inc. **F-27:** "Old Abram Brown" from Friday Afternoons, Music by Benjamin Britten, Words from "Tom Tiddler's Ground" by Walter de la Mare. Copyright 1936 by Boosey & Co. Ltd. ORFF accompaniment by Pearson Education, Inc. **F-28:** "Down by the Riverside" African American Spiritual. ORFF accompaniment © 2002 Pearson Education, Inc. **F-30:** "Shenandoah" Capstan Sea Shanty. ORFF accompaniment © 2002 Pearson Education, Inc. **F-31:** "Camptown Races" Words and Music by Stephen Foster. ORFF accompaniment © 2002 Pearson Education, Inc. **F-33:** "Woke Up This Morning" African American Freedom Song. ORFF accompaniment © 2002 Pearson Education, Inc. **F-37:** "Ah ya Zane" (Zane from Abedeen) Arabic Folk Song. ORFF accompaniment © 2002 Pearson Education, Inc. **F-39:** "Se va el caimán" (The Alligator) Dance Song from Colombia. ORFF accompaniment © 2002 Pearson Education, Inc. **F-41:** "La Jesusita" Folk Song from Mexico. ORFF accompaniment © 2002 Pearson Education, Inc. **F-43:** "St. Louis Blues" Words and Music by W. C. Handy. ORFF accompaniment © 2002 Pearson Education, Inc. **F-45:** "Zum gali gali" Folk Song from Israel. ORFF accompaniment © 2002 Pearson Education, Inc. **G-3:** "Stand By Me" featured in the Motion Picture Stand By Me. Words and music by Ben. E. King, Jerry Leiber and Mike Stoller. © 1961 (Renewed) Jerry Leiber Music, Mike Stoller Music and Mike & Jerry Music LLC. **G-10:** "You've Got a Friend," Words and music by Carole King. © 1971 (Renewed 1999) Colgems-EMI Music Inc. This arrangement © 2001 Colgems-EMI Music Inc. All Rights Reserved. Used by permission. **G-12:** "Río, rio" (River, River) English words © 1964 Silver Burdett Ginn. **G-13:** "Freedom Is Coming" South African Spiritual. Copyright © 1984 by Utryck. Used by permission. **H-6:** "Morning Has Broken." Reprinted by permission of Harold Ober Associates Incorporated. Copyright © 1957 by Eleanor Farjeon. KEYBOARD accompaniment by Pearson Education, Inc. **H-7:** "Adelita" Folk Song from Mexico. KEYBOARD accompaniment © 2002 Pearson Education, Inc. **H-9:** "Home on the Range" Traditional Song from the United States. KEYBOARD accompaniment © 2002 Pearson Education, Inc. **H-11:** "De colores" Folk Song from Mexico. KEYBOARD accompaniment © 2002 Pearson Education, Inc. **H-12:** "Scotland the Brave" Words and music by James Hanley. 1952 (Renewed) Kerrs Music Corp. Ltd. WARNER BROS. PUBLICATIONS U.S. INC., Miami, FL. 33014. KEYBOARD accompaniment by Pearson Education, Inc. **H-13:** "Tumba" Hebrew melody. KEYBOARD accompaniment © 2002 Pearson Education, Inc. **H-14:** "Blow the Wind Southerly" Folk Song from Northumbria. KEYBOARD accompaniment © 2002 Pearson Education, Inc. **H-16:** "Johnny Has Gone for a Soldier," Collected by John Allison. McCarthy, Fingar, Donovan, Drazen & Smith, LLP. KEYBOARD accompaniment by Pearson Education, Inc. **H-17:** "Oh, Watch the Stars" from Folk Songs North America Sings by Richard Johnston. 1984 by Caveat Music Publishing Ltd., copyright assigned 1988 to G. Ricordi & Co. (Canada) Ltd. KEYBOARD accompaniment by Pearson Education, Inc. **H-19:** "Good Mornin', Blues" New words and new music arranged by Huddie Ledbetter. Edited and new additional material by Alan Lomax. TRO- © Copyright 1959 (Renewed) Folkways Music Publishers, Inc., New York, NY. KEYBOARD accompaniment by Pearson Education, Inc. **H-20:** "Down by the Riverside" African American Spiritual. KEYBOARD accompaniment © 2002 Pearson Education, Inc. **H-21:** "Camptown Races" Traditional Folk Song. Words and Music by Stephen Foster. KEYBOARD accompaniment © 2002 Pearson Education, Inc. **H-22:** "¡Qué bonita bandera!" (What a Beautiful Banner!) Folk Song from Puerto Rico. KEYBOARD accompaniment © 2002 Pearson Education, Inc. **H-23:** "La Jesusita" Folk Song from Mexico. KEYBOARD accompaniment © 2002 Pearson Education, Inc. **H-24:** "Cattle Call," Words and music by Tex Owens. © 1943 (Renewed 1971) Forster Music Publisher Inc. This arrangement 1996 Forster Music Publisher Inc. KEYBOARD accompaniment by Pearson Education, Inc. **H-25:** "St. Louis Blues" Words and Music by W. C. Handy. KEYBOARD accompaniment © 2002 Pearson Education, Inc. **H-26:** "Blowin' In The Wind" Words and music by Bob Dylan. Copyright © 1962 Warner Bros. Inc. Copyright renewed 1990 Special Rider Music. KEYBOARD accompaniment by Pearson Education, Inc. **H-27:** "Ríu ríu chíu" Sixteenth-